pcl dcp.

Rediscovering
THE
Art of
Dying

REDISCOVERING
THE
ART OF
DYING

HOW JESUS' EXPERIENCE
AND OUR STORIES
REVEAL A NEW VISION
OF COMPASSIONATE CARE

NUALA KENNY
SC, OC, MD, FRCP(C)

FOREWORD BY
ARCHBISHOP PAUL-ANDRÉ DUROCHER

NOVALIS

© 2017 Novalis Publishing Inc.

Cover image: Getty Images
Layout: Audrey Wells

Published by Novalis

Publishing Office
10 Lower Spadina Avenue, Suite 400
Toronto, Ontario, Canada
M5V 2Z2

Head Office
4475 Frontenac Street
Montréal, Québec, Canada
H2H 2S2

www.novalis.ca

Library and Archives Canada Cataloguing in Publication

Kenny, Nuala P., author
     Rediscovering the art of dying : how Jesus' experience and our
stories reveal a new vision of compassionate care / Nuala Kenny.

ISBN 978-2-89688-451-3 (softcover)

     1. Terminal care--Religious aspects--Christianity. 2. Death--
Religious aspects--Christianity . I. Title.

R726.K456 2017   616.02'9   C2017-902598-8

Printed in Canada.

We acknowledge the support of the Government of Canada.

5   4   3   2   21   20   19   18   17

TABLE OF CONTENTS

Acknowledgements

It has often been said that writing is a solitary activity. Writing this book has been the most intense experience of my life and unlike any other writing I have ever done. This project took over my prayer, thoughts and life for months so that I had feelings of isolation and loneliness in writing this book. At the same time, I have had times of deep peace in finding new meaning in familiar scriptures, and flashes of joy in coming to know that Jesus lives.

My goal for this work was to do something unique in bringing together theological and spiritual reflection of Jesus' experience of suffering and death with patient and family experience of sickness and dying today. I have been privileged to provide clinical care for 34 years and to assist with the many complicated ethical and moral decisions in medicine for another 15 years. Patients and families have been my most important teachers. But I have also been privileged to work with amazing, dedicated colleagues in medicine and health care, and their influence has been profound. The Sisters of Charity of Halifax have been unwavering in their support of my ministry.

I need to give special recognition to Dr. Romayne Gallagher, a palliative care physician and woman of faith, who provided the original inspiration for this work and contributed to the original outline. My now deceased friend Archbishop James M. Hayes encouraged me, saying that this project was something I should and could do. His support and witness to care for the sick and dying carried me through difficult days.

Practically, this book could not have been written without the help and support of my wonderful colleagues in the Catholic Health Alliance of Canada Ethics Network, especially Jim Roche, Fr. Mark Miller, Pat Murphy, Gordon Self, Francis Maza, Christine Jamieson, Chris DeBono, Hazel Markwell, William Sweet, Neil Elford, and Dr. Dave Unger. They shared their own patient stories and helped with ensuring authenticity and clinical accuracy to my stories.

Many other friends and colleagues patiently and prayerfully read chapters, including Fr. Bernard O'Neill, Fr. Anthony Boylan, Rev. Jody Clarke, Marilyn Sweet, Beverly Musgrave, Sister Anne Harvey, Dr. Jean Gray, Dr. Sarah Fung, and a number of other faith-filled friends too numerous to mention. And thanks to Tim Krahn, a faithful research assistant.

I believe that my redeemer lives!

Foreword

The movement to legalize euthanasia around the world compels all to reflect on what it means to die. It also calls for deep reflection on those realities that remind us continually of our finitude and mortality: suffering, illness, dependence and disability. Ultimately, it requires us to ponder the meaning of life itself. In this remarkable book, Sister Nuala Kenny invites us to undertake this reflection with her.

An important turn in my own struggling with these issues arose when I first heard the expression *ars moriendi* – the art or craft of dying – in a talk on palliative care given by Dr. Bernard Lapointe at an annual conference of the Quebec palliative care network (*Réseau de soins palliatifs du Québec*). Dr. Lapointe had gotten involved in palliative care during the AIDS crisis when he became deeply frustrated with traditional medical attitudes towards his dying patients. He worked with and learned from Dr. Balfour Mount, whom many consider to be the father of Canadian palliative care.

In his talk, Dr. Lapointe expressed his worries that palliative care was moving from a holistic approach in the care of patients to a more technical, institutional approach. He shared his fears that palliative care workers today run the risk of focusing so much on the pain to be managed that they forget the man or woman who is experiencing the pain. It is in this context that he suggested that the palliative care movement should endeavour to rediscover a medieval concept, that of the *ars moriendi*.

I was intrigued by this thought and decided to research this concept. I discovered that *Ars moriendi* was the title given to two related books published in Europe in 1415 and 1540 and translated into many languages. These books were the product of dark days when the bubonic plague was slaughtering a third of the population of Europe and priests could not hope to be present at the deathbeds of all their parishioners. A need arose for some kind of guide for laymen and laywomen who wanted to help their loved ones or neighbours prepare for death. At that time, everyone saw death as the moment leading up to one's judgment before God. The risk was great, because the Devil would see this moment as his final chance to steal into a dying person's mind and heart, seduce them and lead them to damnation. The craft of dying lay in knowing the devil's snares and how to avoid them, in order to prepare oneself to meet the judge and Saviour who could finally lead them into paradise.

One remarkable trait of these books, and many similar ones that were to follow in the next centuries, was their emphasis on the active role of both the agonizing man or woman and those who accompanied them to death. It strikes me that the English word "patient," likes its cognate "patience," derives from the Latin verb *patior*, meaning "I suffer, I endure, I submit." From the same Latin root, we derive the English adjective "passive," whose synonyms include lethargic, inert and submissive. Is this not how we tend to see a person, not only in the final stage of life, but when living with serious disease or disability: totally dependent, unable to act or even to decide, at the mercy of whoever happens to be caring for them at that moment?

Yet the very concept of an *ars moriendi* implies that this person, on the contrary, is called to be a living actor, the prime agent in responding to the various challenges involved in living and dying. The idea that there should be a "craft" of dying implies that there is a skill to be applied here. The Latin *ars* is often translated simply as "art," but its meaning is broader, taking in such concepts as skill, technique, power and craft. In the Latinate languages such as Italian, French and Spanish, it has spawned two words that in English are translated as "artist" and "craftsmanship." "Artist" connotes acquaintance with the world of fine arts, academic training and public status. "Craftsmanship" implies a humbler stance, some kind of experience-based apprenticeship, an amateur status that can nevertheless achieve true beauty.

This craft is learned through shared wisdom with the help of mentors who lead the apprenticed to reflect on their own experience as they move through this process. In learning from one's successes and mistakes, in applying oneself to mastering this craft, dying will be one's final creative act in this world. Indeed, do we not all know someone who, in their dying, proved to have been a "master craftsman"?

And are we not all called, here again, to meditate on God's own craftsmanship as reflected in the Passion and death of his only begotten Son, our Lord Jesus Christ? This is precisely the journey Sister Nuala Kenny invites us to undertake with her in this book. With her, we discover that Jesus was not an inert, passive victim of torture and capital punishment. Knowing what was to befall him, he called his friends together and, in the sharing of the Passover meal, revealed to them the meaning of his coming death and gave them a way to recall it from generation to generation. He entered into the process of death fully aware of its horrors, yet willingly embracing it as part of God's will for him. He dialogued with his prosecutor, forgave those who tortured him, made sure his mother would be cared for, and died with a prayer on his lips. This is the *ars moriendi* to which we should all aspire. Even more, it presents us with a deep and rich *ars vivendi*, an art of living.

Our society, however, has become so focused on autonomy, health, comfort and active living that the dependency, sickness, suffering and limitations that attend our daily lives and reach their climax in the last stage of life cannot be faced, much less embraced. We do not want to learn the craft of dying. We want to jump over that stage and get through suffering and death itself as quickly and as painlessly as possible, the same way some people prefer buying a university dissertation to actually researching and writing one, or going to a restaurant instead of preparing and cooking a meal. Our society is much poorer for it, as are the men and women who face death and dying, and those who accompany them.

Crafts are not learned in school but on the stage of life, through experience-based reflection and processes involving the community. Crafts are learned through apprenticeship, and apprentices need mentors. Sister Nuala Kenny is a wonderful mentor. Her background as a doctor and ethicist grounds her insights in advanced studies, rich experience and deep reflection. Her life as a religious devoted to meditation and prayer connects her insights to our Catholic faith tradition, and her reading of scripture enlightens her experience as her questions draw new meaning from scripture. Readers will appreciate how she connects well-known stories from the last days of Jesus to our contemporary experience of disease and dying, of clinics and hospitals, of medical and palliative care. She is a gifted storyteller, and her stories seamlessly weave experience, knowledge, compassion, values, faith and ethics into a marvellous garment that can fit us all. The questions she puts forward at the end of each chapter allow us to appropriate that garment for ourselves and to shape it to our own diverse concrete situations.

This book is a timely gift. As we learn to deal with a world in which euthanasia has become not only legal but socially accepted and – sometimes, tragically – expected, we must go against the flow and intentionally recover our Catholic trad- ition's wisdom about the good death and the craft of dying. The

Greek word *krisis* – from which English has derived "crisis" – speaks of occasion, decision and movement. Sister Nuala has taken hold of this crisis and responded to it by writing a text that will help us all learn to support, foster and protect those who face suffering and disease, dependency and disability, agony and death. In doing so, we will ourselves learn an art that will not only help us enter more fully into our own experience of death and dying, but also help us live more deeply and faithfully every day. May God bless us all as we learn this craft.

+ Paul-André Durocher
Archbishop of Gatineau

Introduction

For we do not have a high priest who is unable to sympathize with our weaknesses, but we have one who in every respect has been tested as we are, yet without sin. (Hebrews 4:15)

This book is a reflection on the meaning of the healing and reconciling ministry of Jesus Christ for the sick, suffering and dying in our post-Christian society. It was born out of my deep personal need for consolation, wisdom and courage after my experience of the legalization of medically assisted death in Canada. Medically assisted death, which includes both assisted suicide and euthanasia, is a cry from our world for a new art of living and of dying and a call to all Christians to respond to the suffering among us with real and active mercy and compassion.

In response to a challenge from the *Canadian Charter of Rights and Freedoms,* a February 6, 2015, decision of the Supreme Court of Canada decriminalized medically assisted death for a stunningly broad range of "grievous" medical conditions, including "illness, disease and disability" causing "intolerable suffering," with no requirement for terminal illness or dying. As a Roman Catholic Religious sister and a physician with experience in pediatrics, palliative care and health care ethics, this practice is deeply contradictory to all I believe in as a physician and as a Christian. My understanding of medicine as an essentially moral practice, not a market one, has been deeply shaken by this decision. Even more crucial, for me, is the depth and breadth of the challenge presented by medically assisted death to the Paschal Mystery – the suffering, death and resurrection of Jesus Christ, and the central belief of the Christian faith.

In the 16 months between the Supreme Court decision and the passage of federal legislation regulating medically assisted death, I was intensely involved in discussions and debates within the medical profession, among Catholic health care providers, ethicists and clergy, and with national and provincial government bodies. I was trying to mitigate the harms of the decision, particularly in the protection of the vulnerable, and in defending the right of conscientious objection to performing assisted death for physicians and faith-based organizations. I was experienced in the complex and often highly contentious world of public policy development, especially when a fundamental moral and ethical issue was at stake. But this experience was more frustrating than anything I had ever experienced. I was deeply saddened by my inability to make any difference. I realized that my arguments against the use of a medical "fix" to end human suffering were unintelligible to a secular society where individual rights and choice trump all other considerations. Notions such as the sanctity of life, salvific suffering and trust in God have lost their meaning in civic discourse. The deep issues of human suffering at the heart of assisted death needed to be presented differently if they are to speak to ordinary human experience today.

One day, in prayer, when I was feeling a real soul-crushing discouragement, I had an epiphany of sorts about my need to change perspective, focus and vocabulary. Pope Francis has noted that we need to

> Remain steadfast in the journey of faith, with firm hope in the Lord. This is the secret of our journey! He gives us the courage to swim against the tide. Pay attention, my young friends: to go against the current;

this is good for the heart, but we need courage to swim against the tide. Jesus gives us this courage! (Pope Francis, 28 Apr 2013)[1]

Medically assisted death presents an urgent opportunity to swim against its powerful tide before it becomes the only understanding of a *good death*. Most Christians are unaware that they will need spiritual buoys and lifelines to assist in this difficult swim. This is not a gentle and predictable tide, but a dangerous riptide, carrying swimmers into the depths before they even know they are at risk. My change in perspective required my own spiritual conversion, and a deeper experience and understanding of Jesus' life, death and resurrection.

My goals for this work are to deepen the understanding of Christians and specifically Roman Catholics about the magnitude of the challenge of medically assisted death, to promote prophetic resistance to the inappropriate use of technology in response to suffering, and to foster prophetic witness from all in the family of the faith in care of the sick and suffering. This book provides reflections for each of us as we face inevitable questions associated with illness, dependence, suffering and dying for ourselves and our loved ones. I offer it to those facing major medical decisions in their experience of an acute health crisis, to those who endure chronic pain and disability, and to those who are living with a terminal diagnosis. I pray it provides support and encouragement to the faithful families, friends and caregivers who accompany the sick, dependent and dying, to those who may be considering medically assisted death, and to the bereaved whose loved ones have chosen it.

THE POWER OF STORIES

Stories provide a new way to engage us. Stories of the experience of illness, dependence and dying offer a dramatic

---

1   All papal quotations are taken from the Vatican website: vatican.va.

change in focus, perspective and vocabulary from rational argument and debate.

We are people of stories, in our lives and in our faith. We listen to news stories on rising from sleep, we recount vacation stories at coffee break, we repeat family stories at reunions and we read favourite stories to children at bedtime with endless repetition. In this world of rapid, ceaseless communication, we tweet very short stories with hashtags and inexplicable signs, but they, too, tell our story. The Christian faith is centred in remembering and repeating the core stories of our faith. Catholics hear the story of Jesus at every Mass.

I decided to use stories of patients and families in these reflections because they help us move into the empathic experience of courageous and faith-filled responses, as well as into the deep – and often overwhelmingly dark and frightening – experiences of illness, dependence, suffering and dying. Stories reach us in the deep places within us, and open us to new and intimate ways of knowing (Polkinghorne, 1998). They can be confessions of love or regret or remorse. They engage us emotionally and move us to joy and awe, fear and anger, commitment and rejection more frequently and more powerfully than lectures or debates. Stories reveal many things, but they also leave much to the imagination.

Medical practice has become aware there are important differences between the classic brief, rigid and neat case history of a patient that the doctor obtains, focusing on symptoms, diagnosis and treatment, and the real, often messy and sad, and sometimes wonderful stories of the patient's experience of the illness (Hunter, 1993). Patient-centred care requires attention to these stories. They tell us far more than the pathology's effects on the body. They tell us how the life story affects the experience of illness, and how the illness affects the patient's life, hopes, dreams and relationships. Stories can provide images and experiences that dramatically demonstrate why the same disease under a microscope is a unique experience of illness in different persons (Kleinman, 1988).

Stories can give voice to things that are not measurable, and that may seem insignificant, but are often at the core of the experience of suffering. A person's life story provides meaning, context and perspective to crisis. Stories can help construct alternative final chapters, restore a sense of identity to the sick, and provide positive endings of hope and a legacy of consolation for the bereaved.

It is not surprising that stories of experiences of illness and dying have been written in great classics of literature, from Tolstoy's *The Death of Ivan Ilyich* and the contemporary stories in Atul Gawande's *Being Mortal* to a genre of modern biographies and autobiographies.

We need stories of illness, suffering and dying that are rooted in our belief that we have a God who so loved us that he sent his only Son to suffer and die for us. Christians have a God who "*sympathize[s] with our weaknesses*" (Hebrews 4:15). We can suffer in communion with Christ and with the tangible support of a community of mercy and compassion. And that makes all the difference.

Gospel stories of Jesus, the Christ

My reflections follow Gospel accounts of "the greatest story ever told," the life, suffering, death and resurrection of Jesus the Christ. The dramatic stories of the New Testament reveal the depth of God's love for us in the life of Jesus through his teaching and his healing and reconciling ministry. The depth of God's love is most clearly demonstrated in Jesus' final journey, the Way of the Cross, through suffering and death to resurrection.

The Gospels are stories of faith, not strict biography as we know it. They were written by different authors, at different times for different audiences. Each author was trying to understand the life and ministry of Jesus, and to articulate the meaning of his life to his disciples. As with all stories of any common event or experience, the four gospels are dependent on personal experience and will have some interesting differences in recalling events. Just think of your own family members' accounts of the same reunion or childhood Christmas!

Jesus himself used stories when he taught in parables, which are metaphors drawn from ordinary life in planting seeds, losing money, raising a wayward child. They require interpretation and do not provide definitions and clear rules.

Each chapter will begin with Jesus' experience, from Gethsemane to resurrection. We explore insights from theology and spirituality on the Gospel accounts, which show us that Jesus of Nazareth is both fully human and fully divine. The approach is influenced by Ignatian contemplation, which encourages us to place ourselves inside the scenes from scripture, and by *lectio divina,* which is a practice of deeply pondering Gospel passages. We are asked not just to read the scriptures but to enter into the experience *with* Jesus and to use our imagination to allow the Holy Spirit to let us see things in a new way.

PATIENT AND FAMILY STORIES

Each chapter reflects on stories based on real patient, family and caregiver experience to present individuals whose lives mirror, in some ways, the Passion of Jesus. I am indebted to the many patients and families I have been privileged to serve in medicine and health care ethics. These stories are not in the first person. I often provide comments from patients and families, but these are my stories. I have tried to be faithful to their experiences, and to give voice to the challenges and graces they have encountered on their journey. In serving patients and their loved ones, I have seen the power of faith, trust in God's love, and hope in the resurrection bring meaning and comfort to those who are ill, suffering and dying. I have also seen the devastation of abandonment, and the hopelessness and despair of many who had lost their faith and trust in God's love and needed our compassion and gentle mercy.

A health care crisis presents unique issues of spiritual and moral meaning. Whether we are religious or not, a health crisis for us or for our loved ones presents challenges to our identity, security and future. With the diagnosis of serious illness, patients and their loved ones embark on a stressful and uncertain journey with no map or GPS to guide them. Difficult practical decisions about treatments must be made in a time of frightening, distracting and disorienting physical distress in unfamiliar environments. All these threats to life and health raise deep questions of meaning and purpose that have been the traditional concerns of religion and spirituality.

Thanks to the advances of modern health care, many of these health care journeys end happily, with recovery and cure. Others begin a seemingly relentless pursuit of treatments with long-term and life-altering consequences. The most challenging journeys are those of terminal illness and dying. So, a threat to health is a time of both stress and grace. Deep questions about the meaning of life, suffering and death can provide a unique time for deepening of personal faith, and for acceptance of the cost of discipleship.

AN URGENT CHALLENGE TO A *GOOD DEATH*

In a simpler time, with limited medical options, death came quickly to most persons. The Christian imagination shared a vision of a *good death* in the death of Saint Joseph. This "righteous man," who lived a selfless life of fidelity to God's call, is comforted and cared for by his loved ones, Mary and Jesus, as he breathes his last. This is a scene of great sadness and loss, but also one filled with a deep peace, and trust in the faithfulness of God.

In medieval times, Christians addressed the challenges of living in preparation for dying through the *ars moriendi,* the *art of dying.* This art leaned heavily upon two fundamental features of the culture: shared faith in the birth, death and resurrection of Jesus, and the importance of families and community in their social organization. Care for the seriously ill and the dying were family and community activities. They accompanied the patient in prayer, sharing stories and laughing and weeping together. A close community bore the painful experience together. While there were very few cures, care and healing happened!

The simple time of Joseph and Mary and the medieval *art of dying* may seem irrelevant to our experiences in the death-denying, death-defying world of modern technologically driven medicine. In reality, the personal, spiritual and communal challenges of dealing with serious illness and dying have become more difficult. The ultimate challenge to the Christian understanding of a *good death* is presented by the legalization and normalization of medically assisted death.

While the media has filled us with vivid images of persons in intractable pain, requesting assisted death, the reality is quite different. Persons rarely request assisted death for pain, but rather for psychological distress and care needs, including uncertainty about the future, desire to control the death, fear of dependence, feelings of loss of dignity, fear of abandonment, and guilt at being a burden to others. These are issues of human suffering. Medically assisted death moves death from a natural, human event in the home and community into a medical act. It is the medicalization of human suffering, but because there is no prescription for suffering, death becomes the treatment.

For Christians, it is a rejection of the Paschal Mystery, the suffering, death and resurrection of Christ. Jesus' suffering is real, but it is also life-giving and redemptive. We do not seek suffering, but through our pain and suffering, we can become sharers in the redemptive work of Christ. As Saint Pope John Paul II reminds us, "In suffering there is concealed a particular power that draws a person interiorly closer to Christ, a special grace" in which there is "above all a call" (*Salvific Doloris*, 1984).

It is our firm belief that

Euthanasia is a false solution to the drama of suffering, a solution unworthy of man. Indeed, the true response cannot be to put someone to death, however "kindly," but rather to witness to the love that helps people to face their pain and agony in a human way. (Pope Benedict XVI, *Angelus,* 1 Feb 2009)

Physician-assisted death is a cry from our world for a new art of living and of dying and a call to witness to real mercy and compassion. Pope Francis reminds us,

An evangelizing community ... has an endless desire to show mercy, the fruit of its own experience of the power of the Father's infinite mercy ... An evangelizing community gets involved by word and deed in people's lives; it bridges distances, it is willing to abase itself if necessary and it embraces human life, touching *the suffering flesh of Christ in others.* ... An evangelizing community is also supportive, standing by people at every step of the way, no matter how difficult or lengthy this may prove to be. (*Evangelii Gaudium*, no. 24)

Physician-assisted death has provided a new urgency for us to touch "the suffering flesh in others." In light of the inexorable movements in support of medically assisted death in the developed world, it is crucial to renew an *art of living* that helps us in our approach to sickness and interdependence and an *art of dying* rooted in Jesus' Passion, death and resurrection.

Today, we have professional groups and health systems to assist the sick and dying as we benefit from wonderful advances in medicine and health care. Unfortunately, this professionalization has fostered complacency about the duties of community. We need to reclaim the duty and obligation of all Christians to care for the sick, dependent, dying and bereaved, and to accompany them in real and active community care.

Today, those of us opposed to physician-assisted death are accused of failure to be compassionate and merciful to the suffering. We are not blind or deaf to situations of great suffering for individuals and families, in health crises and in life itself. But we believe we need to witness to care and accompaniment, not the intentional ending of life. Responding to the challenge, we need the courage to reclaim mercy and to fully respond to *the suffering flesh in others.* "Com-passion" requires the willingness to suffer with others, so a real pastoral conversion is urgently needed.

REFLECTIONS ON SOME STORIES

In Chapter 1, we enter the Garden of Gethsemane with Jesus. We see him collapse in fear, experiencing the natural human desire to avoid suffering. After much prayer, he finds the courage to go on to Jerusalem. He then feels the isolation that comes when loved ones cannot support us in our need. We explore a story of avoidance, turning to denial of serious illness, and the isolation that comes with loved ones' inability to accept dying in another.

Chapter 2 presents Jesus as a condemned prisoner. We see him physically constrained and condemned to death, but still capable of choosing freely *how* to respond to his circumstances, consistent with his life and mission. We reflect on two patients who are faced with major health care decisions and are unsure how to decide what is right.

We are forced to feel Jesus' humiliation as he is stripped of his garment, crowned with thorns and mocked in Chapter 3. We consider the soul-crushing sense of loss of dignity that can result from the ravages of illness, disfigurement and dying. We identify the importance of our responses in fostering or eroding a sense of dignity in the story of an undignified and vulnerable life.

In Chapter 4, Jesus, the "*beloved Son*," now a criminal and an outcast, takes up his cross. We recognize the threat to identity and meaning presented by the losses and constraints of physical illness, disability and cognitive decline. We explore the meaning of loss of physical abilities in one story and ponder the mystery of identity in the tragic experience of a patient with dementia. The relevance of identity as both inherent and relational is considered.

In Chapter 5, the Church's intuitive understanding of the threefold nature of human-physical, psychological and emotional, and spiritual is presented in Jesus' three falls of the traditional Stations of the Cross. Implications for physical suffering and pain control are assessed in our first story. Emotional and psychological suffering is examined in a story of aging and dependence in care needs. Spiritual suffering, which is difficult to diagnose and treat, is revealed in the story of a devout young couple following the tragic loss of their beloved son.

The recruitment of Simon of Cyrene to help Jesus carry his cross, discussed in Chapter 6, demonstrates the need we all have for support and assistance in difficult times. We address the importance of hospice palliative care and some misunderstandings about its role and efficacy.

In Chapter 7, we contemplate Jesus nailed to the cross, losing all apparent control over his circumstances, and now actively dying. We hear his last words and appreciate that he is actively saving us right up to his last breath. Jesus' cry of thirst allows for clarification of concerns about feeding at the end of life.

Reflecting on Jesus' death and total surrender in Chapter 8 provides lessons for our own dying. Here, we explore the pathways of death for many who have never been at a deathbed, and we recognize dying not as a passive reality but as active life completion. We review the moral tradition regarding pain control at end of life, including sedative palliation.

Chapter 9 describes the burial of Jesus. We reflect on the importance of rituals in grief and bereavement. The very different responses of disciples to Jesus' death help us to understand the uniqueness of our grief and mourning. Some implications for a robust ministry of consolation are identified.

The resurrection, where the God of surprises provides the ultimate triumph over suffering and death, is celebrated in our final chapter. Here, we reflect on the stories we have explored and the many untold stories of pain and suffering this reflection has raised. This now is our story. It is the never-ending story of all Christians as we are called to be witnesses to Jesus' triumph over suffering and death, and to alleviate the suffering of others by our words and deeds.

And so our journey with Jesus begins.

I

THE TEMPTATION TO AVOID SUFFERING: JESUS IN GETHSEMANE

"Father, if you are willing, remove this cup from me ..."
In his anguish he prayed more earnestly, and his sweat
became like great drops of blood falling down on the
ground. (Luke 22:42-44)

We begin our journey on the Way of the Cross as Jesus and his disciples move from the Last Supper to the Garden of Gethsemane, the turning point in the story of Jesus' earthly life. Coming from a triumphant entry into Jerusalem, where the chief priests note, *"Look, the whole world has gone after him!"* (John 12:12-19), and the Passover supper, where Jesus gives us the great gift of the Eucharist and predicts the betrayal of Judas and denials of Peter, Gethsemane presents us with two powerful images: Jesus praying in great distress and anguish, and the sleeping disciples he needs for support failing him repeatedly.

Luke uses *agonia* here, translated weakly as "distress," a word not used elsewhere in scripture. Perhaps because we have heard of the agony in the garden so often, we miss the dramatic and graphic scene. We see that Jesus is in agony in the fullest sense of the word; his sweat was "*like great drops of blood.*" This is the fully human Jesus experiencing the natural human desire to avoid pain and suffering. While the details are not completely clear, Jesus knows that incredibly difficult and painful things will be required of him in the days to come. His teaching about the reign of God, as seen in the Beatitudes, has overturned convention. His actions, especially in his cures and his relationships with the poor and marginalized, have scandalized and angered both Jewish and Roman authorities. The anxiety and uncertainty of what is to come are overwhelming, and as Jesus enters the garden, we see a dramatic change in his emotions as "*he began to be distressed and agitated. And he said to them, 'I am deeply grieved, even to death; remain here, and keep awake.' And … he threw himself on the ground*" (Mark 14:33-35).

The English translation of "distress," for the Greek *ekthambeisthai*, fails to capture the original's sense of profound disarray and disintegration with physical manifestation of shuddering. Neither does the use of "fear," for *ademonein*, convey adequately the agitation and deep sense of isolation (Brown, 1994). In Gethsemane, Jesus is not yet experiencing pain or other physical symptoms. That is all yet to come. But he is already the Suffering Servant of scripture, experiencing emotional, psychological and spiritual challenges (Martin, 2014). His agony in the garden helps us focus on the fact that pain and suffering are two distinct realities.

While some see "*he threw himself on the ground*" as Jesus prostrating himself in prayer, other scripture scholars understand the original words used to suggest that Jesus literally collapsed with fear and agitation. Use of the word "*grieved*" to describe his soul suggests that he feels as if the sadness and uncertainty may overwhelm and kill him.

Jesus returned to prayer three times before being able to surrender to God's plan, because he did not seek death or suffering. We can understand his being angry or confused in the circumstances, but Jesus grounds his response in his relationship with the Father, trusting that no matter how difficult and frightening things might become, things will work out for the good. And so he surrenders and responds, "... *yet, not my will but yours be done*" (Luke 22:42).

How was Jesus able to experience this terrified agony and yet surrender this way?

Jesus comes to Gethsemane with a particular personal history that includes how he learned to approach the difficult decisions in life. We know the story of his birth, but almost nothing of the 30 "hidden" years in which he came to adulthood and learned how to cope with difficulty. The scriptures tell us crucially important things about Mary and Joseph. They both responded to the unimaginable things God asked of them with great courage and total trust in God's plan for them. They clearly modelled these attitudes to Jesus.

We do have one amazing insight into the man Jesus was becoming in the only event in scripture from his early adolescence:

And when he was twelve years old, they went up as usual for the festival. When the festival was ended and they started to return, the boy Jesus stayed behind in Jerusalem, but his parents did not know it. Assuming that he was in the group of travellers, they went a day's journey. Then they started to look for him among their relatives and friends. When they did not find him, they returned to Jerusalem to search for him. After three days they found him in the temple, sitting among the teachers, listening to them and asking them questions. And all who heard him were amazed at his understanding and his answers. When his parents saw him they were astonished; and his mother said to him, "Child, why have you treated us like this? Look, your father and I have been searching for you in great anxiety." He said to them, "Why were you searching for me? Did you not know that I must be in my Father's house?" But they did not understand what he said to them. Then he went down with them and came to Nazareth, and was obedient to them. His mother treasured all these things in her heart. And Jesus increased in wisdom and in years, and in divine and human favour. (Luke 2:42-52)

Clearly, from a young age Jesus had a deep interest in things spiritual and the courage to follow what he believed God asked of him, even when it was difficult to accept. From the very beginning of his public ministry, we see Jesus facing difficult issues, from rejection in his own town when he reads from the prophet Isaiah in the synagogue at Nazareth to criticism of his preaching, healing and relationships. So, here in Gethsemane, rather than flee or respond violently, Jesus chooses to surrender not only his will but also his fear and anxiety. All is now in the Father's hands.

FRANK'S STORY OF AVOIDANCE AND DENIAL

Frank, the 48-year-old son of immigrants, spent his preteen years translating English for his Polish parents. He excelled at languages and computers. When he graduated with an MBA, he built a lucrative business. He was successful in work and in life. His wife, Kim, and their two children were his priority. They were well cared for and he always made it home for dinner and for family and children's important activities.

Work was busy, so he ignored the coughing and fatigue for months. His wife finally forced him to seek help when he began to lose weight. A chest X-ray suggested trouble. After weeks of demanding and invasive tests and investigations, he was told he had advanced lung cancer with a very poor chance of even five-year survival. He did not want to hear about statistics. He wanted to deal aggressively with his disease, as he would with any difficult project. When doctors identified a genetic marker indicating a better response to a certain chemotherapy, he interpreted the news as things going his way.

Ten months later he was facing a tougher fight. The cancer had not responded to two gruelling courses of chemotherapy. When the oncologist began to speak of palliative care, Frank interrupted, saying, "I don't give up that easily. What else can you suggest?" Rather than discuss that it wasn't simply a situation of fighting on or giving up, but how he wanted to live for the time he had, the oncologist indicated there was a new research trial of a drug available, if he could afford it. Frank mortgaged the house, enrolled in the trial and began the ordeal of travelling to and from treatments.

Kim supported him wholeheartedly until he was so weak and emaciated that he struggled to walk more than a block. As he lay sleeping, she would look at him and weep because she knew he was dying. He became angry when she tried to talk about what she could see happening, and accused her of betraying him. She could talk to friends about her fears but did not raise them further with Frank for fear of causing a rift in their relationship. She found herself caught up in a conspiracy of silence and the loss of meaningful conversation with him.

Even after the experimental trial drug was stopped and Frank sought unregulated treatment in Mexico, she went with him. But his positive energy and warmth and his care and concern for her and for the children were gone, driven by this obsession to fight the cancer. Kim felt pity for him, but also anger and hurt that his

precious remaining time was spent seeking futile treatment rather than being with her and his worried children
and addressing what was happening to them all.

In both Jesus' experience in Gethsemane and Frank's story, we see vivid examples of the normal human desire to avoid pain and suffering, but with very different responses. Jesus moves from avoidance to acceptance. Frank moves into denial.

Fear and avoidance of physical and psychic harm are basic responses we use to great benefit in surviving difficult situations (Weiten et al., 2008). They are protective for much of our life, keeping us away from risky behaviours that could shorten our life. So, whenever we are threatened, as in a near car collision or a sudden loud noise, our body responds and adrenalin is released, raising our heart rate and providing extra energy to our muscles so we are ready for fight or flight. This protective system is meant to function only occasionally. Excessive and constant alertness is experienced as anxiety. We all know how tiring and frightening anxiety can be and how it can be a major source of our suffering.

While our initial reflex response is to avoid pain and dis-tress, we can respond deliberately and intentionally. We can choose to confront and endure pain and distress for higher reasons, such as when we have difficult, but necessary, conver-sations with estranged relatives, get an immunization or act to save another from risk. We can also respond to pain and distress in harmful ways, turning to drugs or alcohol.

The natural reaction of avoidance can turn to denial when the difficult situation cannot be avoided. Denial is an uncon-scious defence mechanism for coping with fear, guilt, anxiety and a wide range of disturbing realities. We all use it in our personal life as well as in social and political life. Denial can actually help us when we begin to cope with life-threatening information about our health or that of loved ones. It gives us a little breathing space and allows us to come to an acceptance of serious illness and dying in our own time. However, persistent denial in the face of serious threats to life and health becomes a pathology all its own.

We all approach difficult issues with different personalities and unique life histories. Jesus' approach was shaped by the modelling of his earthly parents, Mary and Joseph, and by his deep trust in God. Frank's use of denial is typical of his approach to life's challenges as he overcame difficulties in helping his parents adapt to a new country. He learned when he was young that if he put his mind to it, he could overcome all obstacles. But now his denial of his illness has become a real obstacle to dealing positively with his dying and his obligations to his family.

Kim supports Frank's obsessive pursuit of a cure and denial of reality, even after it becomes a sore point between them, because she doesn't want to be disloyal. She needs professional help, as well as the support of family and friends, to help her deal with her own feelings and concerns, especially related to their children and the toll all this is taking on them. She needs help in getting Frank to understand that his denial of the terminal nature of his illness is damaging relationships with Kim and the children. The denial is harmful and is increasing the pain and suffering of all.

Frank is crying out for help! Can we begin to imagine his terror as he realizes that his way of coping is just not working here, and his recognition of his inability to be the loving and caring husband and father he desires to be? In helping Frank cope, pastoral care may play an important role in helping him address the deeper spiritual issues at stake in his denial and his fear of death.

His health care team hasn't helped him. There was no palliative approach offering psychological and spiritual support from the beginning of his diagnosis (Emanuel & Librach,

2011). There was no discussion of the goals of care or when and how they might change. Many health care providers do explore painful situations gently, and are able to facilitate and enter into difficult conversations. However, too many others signal their own discomfort and anxiety, and even a sense of failure, around death and dying. Frank's oncologist, rather than explore why he would see palliative care as giving up, chooses to suggest unproven therapy. He raises false hope for a magic cure out there.

We know from careful research in end-of-life care that raising the issue of dying in a straightforward and sensitive manner can give patients and families the permission they need to begin to address their fears. Frank can't be forced to abandon his only coping skill. He needs family and caregivers to offer alternatives and be ready to discuss anytime he is ready.

Jesus provides us with a powerful example of moving from the natural avoidance of pain and suffering to trust in the Father's care and plan for us. There is another important scene in Gethsemane. Once Jesus accepts what lies ahead, he returns to his disciples. We reflect now on his experience of isolation when his beloved friends are unable to support him.

ISOLATION AND LONELINESS IN ILLNESS

When he got up from prayer, he came to the disciples and found them sleeping because of grief, and he said to them, "Why are you sleeping? Get up and pray that you may not come into the time of trial." (Luke 22:45-46)

Hearing the graphic description of Jesus' fear and distress, it is no wonder that he needs the support of his friends. He brings three of his closest friends, Peter, James and John – the same three who were with him at the Transfiguration – to be with him as he prays for strength and guidance. After deep prayer, he returns and finds them sleeping. Imagine how he feels as he asks Peter, the one who promised to always be there for him, *"Simon, are you asleep? Could you not keep awake one hour? Keep awake and pray that you may not come into the time of trial; the spirit indeed is willing, but the flesh is weak"* (Mark 14:37-38).

Jesus returns again to prayer and comes back to find his friends asleep twice more. Though the disciples could clearly see that Jesus needs their support, the scriptures tell us *"their eyes were very heavy; and they did not know what to say to him"* (Mark 14:40).

After his third time praying, Jesus comes to accept that he must trust absolutely in the Father's care and plan for him. More confident now, he goes back to his disciples having been strengthened by prayer. He has the apostles get up and go with him.

> *"Are you still sleeping and taking your rest? See, the hour is at hand, and the Son of Man is betrayed into the hands of sinners. Get up, let us be going. See, my betrayer is at hand."* (Matthew 26:45-46)

It is easy for us to criticize the apostles for failing to support Jesus. He recognizes that they were also experiencing great fear and distress, and that *"the flesh is weak."* These close friends see Jesus, their master, who has always remained calm and in control in all kinds of situations, now in agony and collapsed in fear and anxiety. As disciples of Jesus, they, too, are at risk of imprisonment and death and are now very uncertain about accepting the cost of discipleship. They are already grieving in anticipation of his loss.

Jesus had tried to prepare the disciples for difficult things to come. At the anointing at Bethany he warned them, *"For you always have the poor with you, but you will not always have me"* (Matthew 26:11) and

> *he began to teach them that the Son of Man must undergo great suffering, and to be rejected by the elders, the chief*

priests, and the scribes, and be killed, and after three days rise again. He said all this quite openly. And Peter took him aside and began to rebuke him. But turning and looking at his disciples, he rebuked Peter and said, "Get behind me, Satan! For you are setting your mind not on divine things but on human things." (Mark 8:31-33; see also Mark 9:30-31; 10:33-34)

The Passover supper is indeed Jesus' last supper with his friends. There he gives them a clear farewell, but they have great difficulty understanding and accepting what is to come. In Gethsemane, Jesus experiences the consequences of his friends' and loved ones' avoidance and denial of pain and suffering. So his final moments with his disciples are marked by terrifying isolation. Even more painful, before he leaves Gethsemane he is given up by Judas and captured: *"So when he came, he went up to [Jesus] at once and said, 'Rabbi!' and kissed him. Then they laid hands on him and arrested him"* (Mark 14:45-46).

The betrayal comes with a kiss, an act of love! The experience of isolation in his time of need, when even his closest friends seem unable to accept what is to come and support him, compounds Jesus' suffering.

SHIRLEY'S STORY AND THE DENIAL OF LOVED ONES

Shirley, a 76-year-old widow, has felt as if she was on a leash since the home oxygen started. She understood that she needed it now that her chronic lung disease was so bad, but she had never got used to the noise or the way she felt trapped by that long, snaking cord.

She was grateful that her son, Jim, and his wife, Charlene, had moved her to the safety of their house. Jim had tea with her in the basement suite every night, and she would talk of many things: how her life had changed because of her illness; how she missed her husband, Doug, who had died three years ago after a long and distressing hospital stay; and how sad she was that Jim's older sister, Karen, had not visited or called her since her father's funeral, even after Shirley was diagnosed with serious lung disease. A devout person, Shirley had attended the wakes and burials of many of her friends and relatives, and often commented on how they died. Jim, ever the peacemaker and listener, never asked questions or pressed her for direction about what all of this might mean for her own preferences for care at the end.

Over the past few years, Shirley has had increasing difficulty breathing and episodes of pneumonia. But nothing was as severe as this latest episode. In the emergency department, her oxygen level was so low that she was intubated, put on a ventilator and treated in the intensive care unit. After five days of treatment, her lungs were still failing and the doctors were recommending withdrawing the ventilator and moving to comfort care. Jim called Karen, as he felt she should know what was happening despite the estrangement between her and her mother. Because Shirley was confused and not able to make decisions for herself now, others had to decide. Jim felt he knew what his mother would want, but he did not want to make the decision to discontinue aggressive treatment on his own.

Karen was extremely upset that he had not called her earlier. "Haven't you asked for a second opinion? Don't let them turn her off like that! I am on my way and nothing should be changed before I get there or I will sue them. I can see that you are not going to challenge anything!" The anger did not diminish when she appeared in person, causing great distress in the ICU. Jim could sense panic in his sister, but he felt hurt and angry because she had not lifted a finger to participate in their mother's care and had no idea of what mattered to his mother.

Some of the greatest suffering comes from the isolation that terminally ill and dying persons experience when their loved ones persistently avoid their reality, and even actively deny it. We can feel betrayed by friends who abandon us or are unable to face us when we are ill. Being able to let go of those we love is a painful thing, and individuals who are dying grieve leaving their loved ones. Those closest to us can have a difficult, if not impossible, time dealing with serious illness and dying. This denial can unduly influence or even coerce the patient to accept treatments they would otherwise refuse because they feel they must respond to a loved one's need for them not to "give up," even when they themselves are ready to die.

Painful conflicts between family members about appropriate medical decisions for loved ones who can no longer speak for themselves and who did not give direction in advance care planning are some of the most common ethical issues in our hospitals today. They can have lifelong effects on the family.

In her last weeks and months, Shirley gave Jim lots of hints about what was important to her, but he did not directly ask her for her preferences for care if she should become so ill that she could not speak for herself. Families report advance care planning as a wonderful gift for knowing what is important to their loved one. It enables them to speak on the person's behalf with confidence and feel much less burdened by the decision making. If Jim had clearly known his mother's preferences for care, he also would have been able to deal more effectively with Karen's guilt-driven demands for care for her mother.

Jim needs help to understand the source of his sister's demands for futile and invasive treatment. Clearly, Karen needs help to deal with the complex emotions she is feeling because of the stormy relationship with her mother. She is a cause of great distress for her brother and the caregivers, but she, too, is suffering.

In discussions with families who have conflicts over the direction of care, it is important for health care providers not to become drawn into the fray, but to help families come to an understanding of what is most important to their loved one. This is best done by a health care team and may need to involve pastoral care workers, psychologists or social workers.

Rolheiser reflects that in Gethsemane, Jesus readies himself through an agonizing and painful sweat, much like an athlete, in order to face what will be asked of him (Rolheiser, 2015). Jesus knew directly the pain of dissension and denial among loved ones at the time he needs them most. The pain of abandonment in his time of need compounds his suffering. But trusting in the will of the Father, he sets out on the Way to the cross.

QUESTIONS FOR REFLECTION

- What do you feel when you hear Jesus' prayers in Gethsemane?
- What touches you most when you hear Frank's story?
- How do you respond to difficulty?
- What is of most concern to you as you hear the experience of Shirley and her family?
- Have loved ones been with you in your hour of need?
- Have you been a support to others even when it caused you pain and distress?
- What would cause you to sweat blood?

2

FREEDOM OF CHOICE: JESUS IS CAPTURED AND ARRESTED

While he was still speaking, suddenly a crowd came, and the one called Judas, one of the twelve, was leading them. He approached Jesus to kiss him; but Jesus said to him, "Judas, is it with a kiss that you are betraying the Son of Man?" When those who were around him saw what was coming, they asked, "Lord, should we strike with the sword?" Then one of them struck the slave of the high priest and cut off his right ear. But Jesus said, "No more of this!" And he touched his ear and healed him. (Luke 22:47-51)

A crowd armed with swords and clubs is sent by the chief priests to arrest Jesus in a stealthy way at night so as not to cause people to riot during the festival. Judas identifies him to the men by a kiss, the sign of love and affection. As if to emphasize the enormity of the betrayal, nowhere else in the gospels do we have Jesus and his disciples greeting with a kiss.

Jesus is captured and bound after Judas' betrayal in Gethsemane. It is unclear why Judas betrayed Jesus. Luke says, *"Then Satan entered into Judas…"* (Luke 22:3). John mentions

Judas protesting the waste of oil in the anointing of Jesus' feet and suggests greed, but it is not clear what has caused him to not only reject Jesus but play a major role in his painful death (Brown, 1994).

In the chaos that follows, the disciples react with both flight and fight. Some flee and are not seen or heard of again during the Passion. One – John tells us it is Simon Peter – cuts off a servant's ear and is ready to shed blood to defend Jesus. Jesus responds immediately, strongly rejecting the violent response to his unjust arrest, saying, *"Am I not to drink the cup that the Father has given me?"* (John 18:11). Remember that in Gethsemane, he prayed over his options. He decided to accept his Passion.

Jesus is dragged away and spends what must have been an agonizing night in a dungeon-like prison filled with dread for what is to come next. *"When day came, the assembly of the elders of the people, both chief priests and scribes, gathered together, and they brought him to their council. ... Then the assembly rose as a body and brought Jesus before Pilate"* (Luke 22:66–23:1).

When Jesus is brought before the chief priests and elders to find evidence that could allow them to pass the death sentence, he does not enter into the debate but courageously answers, *"I am,"* when asked if he is the Christ (Mark 14:62). Because of his decision to follow the way to the cross, he is able to respond with a calm acceptance. He is then sent bound to Pilate, where it becomes very clear that Jesus has done nothing to merit a humiliating and painful death as a criminal. Pilate acknowledges that Jesus is innocent, but orders his death because he fears public opinion.

> So when Pilate saw that he could do nothing, but rather that a riot was beginning, he took some water and washed his hands before the crowd, saying, "I am innocent of this man's blood; see to it yourselves." Then the people as a

whole answered, "His blood be on us and on our children!"
So he released Barabbas for them; and after flogging Jesus,
he handed him over to be crucified. (Matthew 27:24-26)

Jesus underwent two trials, including inquests with Jewish leaders, Annas and Caiaphas and the Sanhedrin, who find him guilty of blasphemy for admitting that he is indeed *"the Messiah, the Son of the Blessed One"* (Mark 14:61-62). Then the Roman authorities, Pilate and Herod, condemn him for treason because Jesus says to Pilate, *"You would have no power over me unless it had been given you from above"* (John 19:11). These were both times when Jesus might have been set free, but was not. Even the crowd rejects him and chooses the notorious Barabbas for release in Pilate's final attempt to save him. There is no last-minute miraculous reprieve for Jesus.

Jesus' anticipation of rejection and difficult things in Gethsemane is rapidly becoming reality. He now surely experiences a sense of what scourging and crucifixion will require of him, but chooses to accept *"in order to fulfil the scripture"* (John 19:28). Jesus, who calmed the sea and drove out demons, does nothing to save himself, because there is a mysterious call here. Though captured and physically constrained, Jesus chooses to reject a violent response and maintains a dignity and serenity that is remarkable. He freely surrenders to what is to come, trusting in the Father to take care of him, and as necessary to fulfill his mission. He comes to his decisions with a firm attitude of trust in God and a commitment to fidelity to his mission. These values allow him to choose how to respond when it appears he has lost all freedom. Bound and captive, he has no choice to do or act, but witnesses choosing how to be faithful to the Father and his to his mission.

Where and how did he learn this ability to make courageous choices and these attitudes of trust and commitment? Just as with us, Jesus' upbringing was crucial in shaping his values and attitudes. Mary and Joseph raised the fully human Jesus and taught him to trust in God even in unimaginably difficult and frightening circumstances. When as a young woman Mary has a dream/angel come to her, she is surprised, even terrified. The angel assures her, "*Do not be afraid.*" She is at first "*much perplexed.*" She doesn't blindly accept, but asks, "*How can this be? ... let it be with me according to your word*" (Luke 1:29, 30, 34, 38). Mary had to trust that nothing is impossible with God, and had to consent freely to what God was asking! After her yes, long after the angel left her, she had to live that trust and commitment in good times and bad.

Joseph, "*a righteous man*" chosen to protect Mary and Jesus, also has a dream/angel assuring him, "*Do not be afraid*" (Matthew 1:19-20). He is asked to accept the impossible and trust in what God is asking of him. Joseph has no lines in scripture, but this quiet man was chosen to teach Jesus to have confidence in making and acting on decisions. Joseph must have been a remarkable man who spoke with his actions and fidelity, if not words. Both Mary and Joseph are reassured to be unafraid as they say yes to the inexplicable and trust in God's love and plan. This was the nurturing environment in which Jesus "*grew and became strong*" (Luke 2:40) and which helped to shape his fundamental attitudes and values. As Jesus matured, he was "*filled with wisdom*" (Luke 2:40), and developed a habit of turning to God in prayer in times of difficulty.

Just as it was for Jesus, our attitudes and fundamental values are crucial in our own experiences of being captured by serious illness, dependence and death, and in our choices when we experience a health crisis.

HARDEEP'S STORY OF INFORMED CONSENT

Hardeep is a 68-year-old retired school principal who has never been seriously ill. Over the last three years,

his ability to walk had gone from several easy kilo-
metres a day to a few slow and uncomfortable blocks
a day because of lower back pain. His loving wife of 40
years, Karina, noted wryly that their golden years were
rapidly turning rusty as what they initially thought was
age-related arthritis in his back got progressively worse.
Their retirement dreams of hiking trips in Europe and
Australia seemed lost.

When the pain became too severe for over-the-counter
drugs like ibuprofen, Hardeep began regular trips to
his doctor, trying new drugs. In a short time he went
from being someone who rarely went to the doctor to
what he described as a medical "frequent flyer." For
months, his pain was manageable when he was lying
down or sitting, but when he walked for more than a
few blocks it became unbearable, and he needed to
sit until it subsided.

When he began to experience severe pain even when
he was not walking, it was clear that investigations
into the cause were necessary. Hardeep then entered
a gruelling and anxiety-provoking period of medical
investigations in the foreign world of hospitals and
laboratories, with its own language of X-rays and PET
scans and white counts and MRIs. He felt as if his life
was totally dominated by these investigations, and that
he had entered a *terra incognita,* like those on ancient
maps that showed uncharted territory with the warning
"Beware of dragons here!"

He was diagnosed with spinal stenosis, a narrowing of
the spinal canal that was compressing the nerves in his
legs, causing the pain and weakness. What had been
assumed to be age-related arthritis was far more serious; it had no easy cure, and came with the certainty of
limitation in movement in the future. The diagnosis was

overwhelming. Hardeep felt as if he was falling into a void where there were dragons and even worse to fear. Karina was too stunned to do anything but sob quietly and hold his hand.

With the diagnosis clear, decisions had to be made regarding treatment. Medical and surgical options were presented. Hardeep chose to continue with medical management; injections of an anti-inflammatory steroid into his spine helped for a few months. His doctor said his pain could become worse without surgery, and Hardeep was referred to a spinal surgeon who recommended surgery to enlarge the spinal canal and relieve the pressure on the nerves. He was told there was a very good chance that after the surgery he would be less disabled and able to walk more, but there was no guarantee that the pain would be better. The surgeon also talked about a number of terrifying surgical complications, such as leaking of the spinal fluid and serious infection, heart attack or stroke as risks of the anesthetic.

Pain relief was what he most wanted from the surgery. But if he could not get rid of the pain, would it be worthwhile? Normally, Hardeep was very comfortable with making decisions in his life. But this was no straightforward decision promising a magical cure – it was something far more risky and complex!

Jesus was physically captured and bound during his ordeal by those whom he would have expected to protect the innocent, but he was still able to respond in ways consistent with his fundamental identity and values. Hardeep feels that he has, in a very real sense, been captured and condemned by this diagnosis. Accustomed to making big decisions for others, now he has a truly life-altering personal decision to make. He needs to trust others' information and competence.

Informed choice in health care

Hardeep comes to his decision regarding medical options, as we all do, with a unique personal history of values, coping mechanisms and approaches to decision making. Some of us are risk-takers and others are risk adverse; some want lots of information while others do not. The decision-making process itself, in a time of pain, stress and uncertainty, can be a cross of its own. Hardeep generally approaches decisions in a careful, analytic way, and rarely consults others. He is now painfully aware that this is very different from making a reasoned decision about which car to buy. Here, he is very dependent on the provision of credible information regarding the likely benefits and harms of his options. He must trust the professional competence and skill of physicians and surgeons to intervene effectively. He feels he is trapped between a rock and a hard place as he tries to decide what to choose.

In an earlier time, when there were few, if any, medical options and the worldview of the *good* was shared by patients and their doctors, doctors wrote orders for treatments intended to improve the patient's situation, to which patients consented. With the truly paradigm-shifting medical advances of the mid-20th century, including cardio-pulmonary resuscitation, the portable ventilator, immunology and organ transplantation, in increasingly pluralistic societies with differing understanding of the right and the good, a new approach to decision making was needed. The technologies brought unprecedented possibilities of benefit, but also major risks of substantial harm.

In both the Catholic tradition and modern bioethics, patients like Hardeep, who are competent to make their own decisions, are the primary decision makers when it comes to the doctor's proposed evidence-informed treatment and care options. This approach respects the patient's dignity and autonomy. For this reason, information regarding a patient's values, beliefs, commitments, wishes and hopes – their life story – is as crucial to making health care decisions as information about the patient's physical condition and laboratory findings.

In this secular context, dominated by autonomy, rights and choice, modern bioethics emerged and rapidly replaced traditional medical ethics. Bioethics became dominated by the principles approach (Beauchamp and Childress, 1994). The dominant principles are respect for autonomy, beneficence (acting for the patient's good), non-maleficence (minimizing harm), and justice or non-discrimination in responding to health care needs. These principles were not ordered by moral importance, but respect for autonomy almost immediately became the trumping principle. For pluralist societies, this approach has the advantage of being distinct from any particular religious or philosophic tradition. It has the distinct disadvantage of being uprooted from a coherent set of fundamental beliefs of the right and the good.

Respecting patient autonomy is about more than decisional competence; it includes respecting the person and their unique life story. Informed choice, which includes both consent and refusal, is the main tool for respecting patient autonomy. Informed choice requires that the patient have the information they need to make a decision presented in a manner they can understand; the capacity or competency to judge the consequences of the information for them and their life story, and freedom from undue fear, influence and coercion.

Information should include the diagnosis, the prognosis (what is likely to happen as the illness progresses) and the anticipated benefits, and possible risks and potential harms of various options, including the option of treating the symptoms associated with illness while refusing aggressive attempts at cure.

Hardeep wants as much information as possible and has even researched spinal stenosis on the internet. As an educator, he recognizes that the interpretation of statistics on benefits, risks and harms is complex, and that the variety of sources of information is both overwhelming and frightening. He tries to get authoritative medical information and is well aware of the direct-to-consumer drug advertising and celebrity endorsement of drugs and devices rampant in the media and on the internet. The more frustrated he gets when he finds no risk-free guaranteed treatment for his condition, the more he checks out these non-validated sources. He has also learned that the risk of harm is distinct from the harm itself. A risk is a high or low probability of a harmful effect. A harmful effect can be minor, like a rash and itching, or major, as in total paralysis or death. Hoped-for benefits, risks and harms all need to be taken into account as he decides what to choose. There are no guarantees of success or satisfaction in health care interventions like those we get with a new car.

The way we are given a diagnosis matters. There are different styles of physician communication and interaction. Some styles focus on the data and fail to address the difficulty in its interpretation. Giving bad news is difficult for doctors. Many overestimate the hoped-for benefits, and some avoid difficult decisions about finitude and the inevitable limits of medicine (Buckman, 1993). Doctors provide information about the evidence on likely effects. Only the patient can decide if the likely effects are, for them, benefits and worth the potential risks and harms of medical interventions. Doctors and their patients can have very different ideas about what counts as a benefit or an acceptable risk. Recent vivid and highly popular patient stories by talented physician-authors Ira Byock (2013) and Atul Gawande (2014) have helped raise awareness of the lived complexity of medical decisions. Hardeep is having his own experience of this complexity as he tries to decide what option to choose.

HEALTH DECISIONS AND THE CATHOLIC TRADITION

Hardeep is a practising Catholic. Many of his fundamental values have been shaped by his faith. He has a loving wife and strong community support for whatever is to come. And there is a long and strong Catholic moral tradition of decision making in illness and dying that can support him in his assessment of benefits and risks (Ashley & O'Rourke, 1997). His pastor has assured him of Church teaching that "Life and physical health are precious gifts entrusted to us by God. We must take reasonable care of them, taking into account the needs of others and the common good." (*Catechism of the Catholic Church*, 1993, no. 2288).

He is trying to make a decision for reasonable care of his health and well-being. While many health care decisions are straightforward, others, such as the one facing Hardeep, are anything but clear and easy. The only choices here are hard choices. He prays over it and decides to try for pain relief to help him deal with this condition. He chooses surgery with its possibility of giving him an opportunity for walks with his beloved Karina, even if they might be short strolls in the local park and not challenging global treks. Fortunately, he has a good, if not perfect, result and is grateful for the improvement.

COLLEEN'S STORY OF REFUSAL OF CARE

Colleen is a 32-year-old single woman who has lived with the diagnosis of cystic fibrosis since infancy. Shortly after birth, she had a life-threatening bowel obstruction. Her parents called her their miracle girl because she survived against all odds, even as the diagnosis of cystic fibrosis was identified as the cause. Committed to seeing that Colleen would live as long and as normally as possible with this life-shortening genetic disease, they began the demanding medical regime of clinic visits, nebulizers, physiotherapy, exercises, antibiotics and nutritional supplements to compensate for malabsorption and to prevent lung infections.

Colleen has always lived with her parents, who are now in their 70s. They and her older brother, Tom, were all involved in her care. She felt loved and supported and practised her faith. She was "a fighter" who excelled at school, graduated from university and got a job as a proofreader. Over the past few years, her lung function has deteriorated, and she is now breathless after mild exertion. She has had frequent hospitalizations for severe infections and has needed a ventilator to help her breathing while she recovered. The staff had begun to talk to Colleen about her desires and wishes for future care, and she began to express concern that medicine was no longer able to give her more good days than bad ones. They noted that she put on a show of courage and optimism whenever her parents were visiting, but had lost the joy of life.

Her parents were insistent on doing everything possible and wanted Colleen to pursue a lung transplant. When she was told she was too sick for a transplant, she accepted it. She told Tom that she was tired of being tired and short of breath. She was tired of having to be "a fighter," but swore him not to tell their parents because she did not want to disappoint them after all they had done for her.

A few days ago, she collapsed after only two weeks at home. She was again admitted to the intensive care unit. She was diagnosed with widespread infection: sepsis. "I think it is time," she said to the admitting physician. But rather than asking what she meant, he reassured her that he was starting antibiotics. Within hours of admission, she went into shock and became unresponsive.

As usual, her parents were at her bedside in the ICU and demanded that the staff do everything possible. Tom tried to tell his parents what Colleen had shared with him, and the staff tried to share their concerns. However, despite having a life-limiting condition, Colleen had never done advance care planning and before she became unconscious had not made a formal decision to refuse further aggressive treatment. Tom did not have formal substitute decision-making authority. The medical staff defaulted, as they always do in these situations, to aggressive interventions. Because of the overwhelming infection in Colleen's weakened state, her kidneys were now failing and she needed renal dialysis to survive.

The ICU team arranged for a family meeting. Despite overwhelming evidence that she was dying, her parents would not agree to discontinuing aggressive medical care and shifting to comfort care. They believed she would overcome this crisis and prove the doctors wrong, as she had done so many times before. They believed that God would take her when he was ready and that their faith required they do everything possible to prolong life.

REFUSAL AND WITHDRAWAL OF MEDICAL INTERVENTIONS

Colleen comes to her health crisis with a very different life history from Hardeep, who has been healthy and well his whole life. Moreover, she comes with a limited experience of making truly independent decisions. Her values and attitudes about risk and benefit and medical technology have been shaped by her lifelong fight with cystic fibrosis. She and her family have seen her as a successful survivor against all odds. But after 32 years, she is tired of fighting and is unable to let her loving parents know how she really feels.

Informed choice in health care includes both informed consent to a proposed intervention and informed refusal. Like informed consent, informed refusal requires that Colleen have the information she needs to make this decision, the capacity or competency to judge the consequences of refusal of aggressive care, and freedom from undue fear, influence and coercion in making the decision. Colleen has more than enough information about cystic fibrosis and its course. When she balances the risks and benefits of further interventions towards cure, it is not a theoretical exercise. She has unique experiential knowledge of the disease and what medicine can wonderfully do and sadly cannot do. Unfortunately, Colleen has not felt free to share her real fears and wishes with her parents because of her desire not to disappoint them after all their faithful care over her life. In a real sense, she is not free to decide as she would want. The family conspiracy of silence about her dying young and her desire to protect her parents means she has not had the opportunity to address her inevitable dying directly. Now, she is unconscious and no longer capable of making decisions. Her parents, brother and health care team, including nurses who have been with Colleen many times over the years, are at odds about the right thing to do.

Because Colleen did not do advance care planning and formally appoint a substitute decision maker, she is now in a decisional limbo, with the distinct possibility of long-lasting conflict and distress among her family members, no matter what decision is made. Her parents are caught in an overwhelmingly painful situation because, no matter the age, the death of a child is an unimaginable loss. They have always felt guilty about Colleen's health needs, especially about cystic fibrosis being an inherited disorder. In a very real sense, their family life has been overshadowed by care for Colleen. They desperately need to be reassured that they have been good parents, but need to recognize that medical technology, which has been so life-saving for Colleen, is now death-prolonging. They need to be helped to hear from others the wishes and fears Colleen could not share with them. Their faith should be a support to them now, not a source of guilt.

Many Catholics, like Colleen's parents, mistakenly believe that Catholics are required to do "everything possible" to stay alive as long as possible. They need to understand that they are not obliged to do everything possible to prolong biological life. The Church teaches clearly that "If morality requires respect for the life of the body, it doesn't make it an absolute value" (*Catechism of the Catholic Church*, no. 2289). It follows, then, that "Life and physical health are precious gifts entrusted to us by God. We must take *reasonable care* of them, taking into account the needs of others and the common good" (*Catechism of the Catholic Church*, no. 2288).

Over centuries, the Catholic faith has developed ways of thinking about what "reasonable care" means. In principle, it includes interventions that are readily available, effective and not excessively burdensome. The interventions are valued because they allow the patient to pursue life goals, relationships with others, spiritual goods and, ultimately, union with God. The Church's understanding of "reasonable care" has never required individuals to accept interventions that they experience as too burdensome, even if such therapies provide some benefit. When the demands of life-sustaining interventions cause spiritual concerns, obstruct relationships or create emotional and psychological burdens, they may be withdrawn or declined. Colleen has taken more than reasonable care over her lifetime. The Church teaches that, when death is clearly imminent and inevitable, one can in conscience "refuse forms of treatment that would only secure a precarious and burdensome prolongation of life, so long as the normal care due to the sick person in similar cases is not interrupted" (*Evangelium Vitae*, 1995, no. 65).

Colleen could, in good conscience, refuse the continuation of aggressive but now futile care. Her grieving parents need to accept her wishes. As they do so, they need the support of their faith and of a caring and consoling community.

Advance care planning as a spiritual activity

When done well, advance care planning is a profoundly spiritual activity. It starts in a deep reflection on the patient's values and beliefs. It involves loved ones learning the difficult task of speaking for the patient when they lose the capacity to speak for themselves, and so it requires deep conversations on painful things. Advance care planning is essential today for anyone with serious and life-threatening disease and for all who are elderly.

Advance care planning should not be a solitary activity. It is profoundly relational and covenantal, not just legal and contractual. It is totally compatible with the Catholic tradition of deciding to forgo extraordinary means and the principles of dignity of the human person, the duty to preserve life, the fact of finitude and the uniqueness of the individual (Sulmasy, 2010). The appointment of a proxy or substitute decision maker to speak for persons when they are not able to speak for themselves is preferred to an instructional directive, called a living will, because it returns decision to the family and friends and allows them to take into account the unique circumstances. Substitute decision makers need education in their duty, which is to speak for the person as the person would want, not as the substitute would want.

Advance care planning directs the use of technology and helps relieve both the burden of decisions in difficult times and conflicts between family members over the right thing to do, such as we see with Colleen's loved ones. While most seriously ill patients have thought of their death, few of them have discussed this with their families or caregivers, and fewer still have completed formal processes.

Difficulty with advance care planning discussions should not surprise us. Jesus himself tried to prepare the apostles for what was to come and for his inevitable death. He has a special last supper and talks to his disciples about what is to come:

"The Son of Man is to be betrayed into human hands, and they will kill him, and three days after being killed, he will rise again." But they did not understand what he was saying and were afraid to ask him. (Mark 9:31-32)

The disciples, like Colleen's parents, were afraid to ask Jesus what he meant because they knew the answer would be their worst nightmare. Church teaching supports the need for reflection on the finitude of human life and for preparation and planning for our dying:

Human life, however, has intrinsic limitations, and sooner or later it ends in death. This is an experience to which each human being is called, and one for which he or she must be prepared. (Pope Benedict XVI, *Message for the Fifteenth World Day of the Sick*, 11 Feb 2007)

Sharing our values and deepest hopes is a way of helping our loved ones to understand how to make decisions for us if we are not capable. It requires us to be clear about our beliefs and hopes.

QUESTIONS FOR REFLECTION

- As you reflect on Jesus' freedom to choose how to respond despite being condemned to death and bound, what challenges arise for you?

- What are the critical issues for you in Hardeep's story?

- How would you respond to Colleen? Her parents?

- If you have faced a serious health issue, how did you decide what to do? If you have never experienced a serious health issue, how would you want to respond?

- What history, personality traits and coping strategies could be an asset to you in serious health decisions? Could these traits and strategies cause you difficulty?

- What are the lessons for us in our support of friends and loved ones making serious medical decisions?

3

Loss of Dignity: Jesus Is Stripped and Mocked

Those who passed by derided him, shaking their heads and saying, "Aha! You who would destroy the temple and build it in three days, save yourself, and come down from the cross!" In the same way the chief priests, along with the scribes, were also mocking him among themselves and saying, "He saved others; he cannot save himself." (Mark 15:29-32)

Then they spat in his face and struck him; and some slapped him, saying, "Prophesy to us, you Messiah! Who is it that struck you?" (Matthew 26:67-68)

Jesus experienced physical abuse during his way to the cross. He was also subjected to profound disrespect, degradation and public humiliation during his ordeal (Brown, 1994). The Jewish authorities mocked him for claiming to be a prophet. In a cruel parody of a children's game of guessing who hit you, they taunt and test Jesus' abilities as a prophet.

He also endured being spit upon in contempt and outrage for blasphemy. In the Old Testament, spitting is a degrading punishment for the guilty.

> *Then the soldiers led him into the courtyard of the palace (that is, the governor's headquarters); and they called together the whole cohort. And they clothed him in a purple cloak; and after twisting some thorns into a crown, they put it on him. And they began saluting him, "Hail, King of the Jews!" They struck his head with a reed, spat upon him, and knelt down in homage to him. After mocking him, they stripped him of the purple cloak and put his own clothes on him.* (Mark 15:16-20)

After his trial, Roman soldiers also abuse and cruelly mock him for claims that he is "*the King of the Jews.*" They dress him in royal purple and a crown of thorns. Their "Hail' is clearly a mockery of "Hail, Caesar!" The mockery turns to abuse as they, too, strike him and spit on him. Jesus knew well what it was like to be an object of contempt and disgust. He felt the humiliation of being the target of cruel and contemptuous humor.

Feelings of humiliation and loss of dignity are common in serious, chronic and terminal illness. The disfigurement of disease and treatments, and dependence on others, especially for help with intimate care needs, brings the risk of loss of dignity to all. Patients who come to health issues with healthy, intact self-esteem experience this loss. Vulnerable populations are at even greater risk.

ELLIE'S STORY OF VULNERABILITY AND INDIGNITY

At the age of 37, Ellie's already shaky and marginalized existence was further undone by a diagnosis of advanced cervical cancer. She had a radical hysterectomy, where the gynecologist removed her uterus and much of the surrounding tissues. Ellie, in the wry, bordering on sarcastic, way she communicated most of the time, reflected that life had "gutted her" as a person and as a woman many times before, but this was the "ultimate evisceration."

Born into considerable privilege, Ellie's early years were magazine perfect. They included private schools, lavish family vacations, the doting attention of her socially acceptable, church-going grandparents, parents and much older brother. She wanted desperately to please her family but felt that she never lived up to their expectations. By the time she was 14, her parents' frequent admonition, "To whom much has been given, much will be demanded," became the standard for her rebellion.

Ellie could recount the harsh facts of the history that "set her apart" from her family: a pregnancy at 16, marriage to her son's father at 17, a second son at 18, episodic substance abuse, poverty and domestic violence where she described herself as a "cheap and available punching bag." She described her life as the kind of "chaos that makes for a good soap opera." Her family regularly offered lifelines, but Ellie believed "I had no way back to them … I did this to myself … I am a disgrace to them."

Ellie was forced to accept help from her family when her teenage sons discovered their father's body, lifeless from a drug overdose, in the basement of their home. She gave over the care of her children to her brother and began the slow work of recovery. She courageously dealt with her substance abuse, upgraded her education and found employment as a paralegal in the law firm of a family friend, but was always fearful that others saw her as "damaged goods." Her sons maintained a tenuous relationship with her. Ellie says that even after she cleaned up, she played the family role of "the loser relative with a shady past."

She was making progress when she was assaulted again – by the cancer diagnosis. Following surgery, Ellie received both chemotherapy and radiation therapy; these created fistulas that caused leakage of urine and stool through her vagina. She began to speak of herself as an "untouchable" by personal and professional caregivers. Her final indignity was in her need for very intimate personal care. She despaired that the cervical cancer stigmatized her in the eyes of the nurses and doctors because of its association with sexual activity.

After transfer to a chronic care facility, Ellie's world was limited to her hospital room and adjacent bathroom. "Pretty crappy real estate, don't you think?" was her opening line to most visitors, who rarely saw Ellie face to face. Her blanket-shrouded back was familiar to all. She refuses to eat because she doesn't want "to spend the time I have left on the toilet." Ellie believes it is fate that her "crappy life" is going to end in a medical condition where she is constantly unclean. She has lost all sense of dignity and of herself as a person worthy of care or attention.

THE LOSS OF DIGNITY

The experience of loss of dignity is common in serious and chronic life-limiting illness. This loss is most keenly felt when patients need help with intimate care needs, develop disfiguring changes in their appearance or abilities, or have symptoms that interfere with normal social functioning. Because Ellie has all of these risk factors, some sense of a loss of dignity is not surprising. But Ellie does not come to this health crisis from a healthy sense of self-esteem. Her suffering is intensified by a life story that has made her vulnerable to a devastating sense that she is not worthy of care and respect. Ellie's entire adult life has eroded her sense of dignity and personal worth. Restoration of her dignity is now a crucial goal of care. In fact, all care for Ellie will be limited in its ability to provide comfort if this loss of dignity is not recognized and addressed.

THE MANY MEANINGS OF DIGNITY

Dignity is a complex concept with many meanings in philosophy and theology. Far from being just a theoretical notion, the promotion and preservation of dignity are essential elements of respectful and effective health care (Pellegrino et al., 2009).

Dignity emerged as an explicit issue in health care ethics in the 1970s in discussions about dying and the right to "die with dignity." There, the notion of dignity was directly tied to autonomy, rational choice and control (Kass, 2002). To this day, one of the major reasons people request assisted death is their sense of a loss of dignity in the experiences of serious illness and dying. So, it is crucially important to understand the meaning and experience of dignity for patients coping with illness, dependence and dying, and the consequences of the sense of loss of dignity for whole person care.

Paradoxically, while clinicians and pastoral care workers try to understand dignity in care, others question whether dignity has any role and judge it to be a "useless concept" that adds nothing to meaningful conversation (Macklin, 2003). There are different understandings of dignity. In antiquity, *dignitas* conveyed the notion of excellence worthy of esteem. Biblical understandings are rooted in the belief that human beings are made in the image of God, and so all share in a God-given dignity. In Kantian moral philosophy, all humans possess dignity because of their rational autonomy and the shared human capacity to set our own goals and ends. Modern constitutions and declarations of rights, including the 1948 United Nations Universal Declaration of Human

Rights, affirm belief in the dignity and worth of the human person, but don't define dignity. The notion of human dignity challenges us to think deeply about human beings and their value and uniqueness.

Theoretical understandings of dignity will guide whether and how we think about it in our care of sick and suffering persons like Ellie. However, theory about dignity is not the same thing as the personal experience of human dignity. We need to understand more deeply what persons mean when they experience a loss of dignity generally, and in health care in particular. We need to understand and resist the attitudes and practices that erode the sense of dignity. We need to foster and adopt those attitudes and practices that promote and conserve human dignity.

THE EXPERIENCE OF DIGNITY

Dignity is important not just at the hour of our death but, as we see with Ellie, in our living. The notion of dignity overlaps with notions such as pride, self-respect, well-being, worth, and self-esteem. In ordinary circumstances, dignity is understood as something far more than just control and rational choice. Over a lifetime, dignity and worth can be honoured and promoted or compromised and eroded. Even those who come to health care crises with a healthy, unbroken sense of their inherent dignity and personal worth can experience the indignity of illness and dependence. For others, like Ellie, their often undignified life experiences have deformed or crushed any sense of personal dignity. Life stories of physical, emotional and sexual abuse, poverty and social marginalization uncover constant threats to a sense of dignity, making them highly vulnerable to further erosion of a sense of worth and sense of having lost their place in the human community.

In serious illness and in dependence for care needs, loss of privacy, forced intimacy with strangers and intrusion into the private areas of life, such as help with bathing and toileting, are guaranteed to be embarrassing and undignified experiences. When the medical condition causes disfigurement or exceptionally unpleasant and humiliating symptoms, such as incontinence, the empathic and respectful response of caregivers is essential.

Each patient's life story is utterly unique and will profoundly influence their illness experience. Ellie's history of brokenness and marginalization, both self-imposed and socially isolated, brings a special vulnerability to her experience with caregivers. Deep listening is essential to get beneath her apparent indifference. Her courage in dealing with her problems needs to be recognized. Her dignity is promoted when we honour her ordeal and promote the resilience she has shown.

PRESERVING AND PROMOTING DIGNITY

Some pioneering and crucially important work on "dignity-preserving care" has been done by Dr. Harvey Chochinov (2012). His research has focused on understanding what is meant by loss of dignity and which attitudes and practices foster dignity or erode it in serious and terminal illness. Three general themes requiring attention have emerged: illness-related concerns, a dignity-conserving repertoire and a social dignity inventory. Using these themes as a guide, we can appreciate crucially important information about Ellie and her care needs.

Illness-related concerns include cognitive and functional capacity, the level of independence, the degree of symptom distress, uncertainty regarding the future, and death anxiety. Ellie is fully aware of her situation. She has a high degree of symptom distress, which has forced her to accept care from strangers. In her sarcastic way, she indirectly refers to dying often, but has not directly addressed the issue with anyone.

The identified elements in a "dignity-conserving repertoire" include perspectives and practices. Positive perspectives include continuity of self, role preservation, generativity and legacy, maintenance of pride, hopefulness, control, acceptance and resilience. The most helpful practices for preserving dignity are living in the moment, maintaining normalcy and seeking spiritual comfort. Ellie is especially vulnerable to the loss of dignity because she comes to her cancer experience with few of the elements of the "repertoire" available to her. She has lost a sense of self, lost her pride and believes she has failed as a daughter to her parents and as a mother to her children.

The social dignity inventory includes consideration of privacy boundaries, the strength of social support, sense of being a burden to others and aftermath concerns. Privacy boundaries are regularly breached in Ellie's care. More importantly, she has cut herself off from the support of her family. Without reconciliation, she will die isolated and alone.

All these issues need to be taken into account to restore a sense of dignity and worth to Ellie in her final days. Her life may have been lived without dignity, but her dying can be truly dignified. At least three things become priorities now. First, what Chochinov calls the "tenor of care," which is created by our attitudes and responses, becomes extremely important. Ellie will see our respect and appreciation of her inherent dignity in our eyes even more clearly than in our physical care. Then, efforts must be made to accompany and to assist Ellie in reconciling with her family. Finally, every effort must be made to create the conditions that foster Ellie's strengths and resilience. Her courage in overcoming drug abuse and educating herself needs to be recognized and honoured.

Dignity and spiritual comfort

Ellie unexpectedly found a source of respect and support from a member of the facility's pastoral care team. Jane is a

Catholic palliative care visitor. She struck up a conversation with Ellie when visiting another resident. Despite Ellie's well-rehearsed resistance, over time, Jane found a way to create a relationship with Ellie. In these regular visits, Jane engaged with Ellie on her own terms and they immediately bonded. Jane became a presence in Ellie's life in a manner that communicated she would not abandon Ellie even if Ellie gave up on herself.

Seeking and receiving spiritual comfort is clearly identified as a helpful practice in promoting and conserving the sense of dignity and in supporting persons with terminal illness. As part of her rebellion against her parents' values and practices, Ellie had rejected the Catholic faith. She has few spiritual resources to bring to her ordeal. She tells Jane that she would like to have God in her life again, but feels she is "too far gone."

Jane gently develops a relationship with Ellie and assures her that no one is "too far gone" and that dignity is an inherent quality of the children of God, not an attribute lost in weakness. Her dignity as a human person is rooted in her creation in the image and likeness of God: "*So God created humankind in his image, in the image of God he created them, male and female he created them*" (Genesis 1:26-27). And the Church teaches that "The dignity of man [*sic*] rests above all on the fact that he is called to communion with God" (*Catechism of the Catholic Church*, no. 27).

Jane shares many New Testament references to our being made in the image and likeness of God, as well as to our being the children of God. She helps Ellie see that all human beings, even those broken in body and soul, are made in the image of God. This belief helps us see dignity where others may see only ugliness and brokenness. One afternoon, just before Easter, Jane brings a booklet on the Stations of the Cross. Ellie becomes totally immersed in Jesus' experience. She tells Jane, "I had no idea this happened to Jesus."

On Easter, Jane brings Ellie an old holy card depicting Jesus' cure of the woman with the hemorrhage. This woman, after long, painful and unsuccessful treatments under many doctors, comes to Jesus but does not think herself worthy to even speak to him and ask for a cure,

> *Then suddenly a woman who had been suffering from hemorrhages for twelve years came up behind him and touched the fringe of his cloak, for she said to herself, "If I only touch his cloak, I will be made well." Jesus turned, and seeing her he said, "Take heart, daughter; your faith has made you well." And instantly the woman was made well.* (Matthew 9:20-22)

Ellie begins to cry and says, "I am just like her. Maybe there is hope for me."

QUESTIONS FOR REFLECTION

- What are your feelings as you hear how Jesus was mocked and degraded?

- As you listen to Ellie's story, what responses would you want to give to her?

- What is your most powerful experience of loss of dignity and self-worth?

- What were the factors that helped you restore your sense of dignity?

- How sensitive are you to attitudes and practices that undermine the dignity and self-esteem of others?

4

Identity Loss in Illness and Cognitive Decline: Jesus Takes up His Cross

So they took Jesus; and carrying the cross by himself, he went out to what is called The Place of the Skull, which in Hebrew is called Golgotha. (John 19:16-17)

Since his time with the elders in the Jerusalem synagogue during the Passover of his twelfth year, to his declaration in the synagogue in Nazareth that the reading from the prophet Isaiah about the blind seeing, the oppressed going free and the good news to the poor had been fulfilled in their hearing, Jesus had a growing sense of who he is. This sense of identity is strengthened at his baptism by John in the Jordan:

… Jesus came from Nazareth of Galilee and was baptized by John in the Jordan. And just as he was coming up out of the water, he saw the heavens torn apart and the Spirit descending like a dove on him. And a voice came from heaven, "You are my Son, the Beloved; with you I am well pleased." (Mark 1:9-11)

It was confirmed again when

… Jesus took with him Peter and James and John, and led them up a high mountain apart, by themselves. And he was transfigured before them, and his clothes became dazzling white, such as no one on earth could bleach them … Then a cloud overshadowed them, and from the cloud there came a voice, "This is my Son, the Beloved; listen to him!" (Mark 9:2-7)

Jesus comes to confidently and intimately call God "Abba," Father.

The question of identity is raised by Jesus himself: *"he asked his disciples, 'Who do people say that I am?'* They responded by naming prophets. He goes on: *"But who do you say that I am?"* They answered him, *"You are the Messiah."* And he sternly ordered them not to tell anyone about him" (Mark 8:27-30). In chapter 2 we heard Pilate's question, *"Are you the King of the Jews?"* Jesus does not deny this identity, but responds with *"You say so"* (Matthew 27:11-12).

Jesus had multitudes flocking to him to hear his message and be cured. He entered Jerusalem to the adulation of the crowds waving palm fronds and hailing him. But here, just a few days later, Jesus, the popular healer, the *"beloved Son,"* is now a condemned criminal and an outcast. His identity, both who he is and his role in salvation history, is now challenged.

For some, Jesus' humanity is difficult to accept; for others, his divinity presents challenges. As fully human, he matures and grows in self-awareness, just as we do. Scripture scholars agree that there are several gospel passages that show this growth in Jesus' understanding of his identity, which reaches its ultimate point in his surrender on the cross and fulfillment in the resurrection (Martin, 2014). Identity is who we know ourselves to be and whom others know. It is complex and ineffable, even sacred. And in some truly mysterious way, taking up the cross is essential to Jesus' identity.

Then Jesus said to his disciples, "If any want to become my followers, let them deny themselves and take up their cross and follow me. For those who want to save their life will lose it, and those who lose their life for my sake will find it." (Matthew 16:24-25)

Being captured, constrained and changed by physical and emotional pain challenges our identity in profound ways. Many persons today facing serious physical and cognitive illness can identify with Jesus' experience.

JOCELYN'S STORY OF LOSS OF TALENT AND LOSS OF SELF

Jocelyn was a single 28-year-old free-spirited and talented artist whose work was just beginning to attract attention and local gallery showings. Growing up in a difficult home environment, with many family and school moves, she was always a bit of a loner. She lost herself in artwork and found security in her identity as an artist.

She became a very popular art teacher in the local school system. She travelled from school to school on a regular schedule. She loved the children and felt it was a great gift to pass on her love of art to them. At the beginning of summer vacation, just as she was getting down to some serious painting, she noticed some weakness in her right hand and experienced visual problems that made it difficult for her to paint. When she began dragging her right foot, she sought medical attention and was referred to a neurologist. The referral took several months; in the meantime, she resumed her teaching, although her problems were getting worse. She finally saw a neurologist and, after weeks of gruelling tests, was given a diagnosis of a severe form of multiple sclerosis. She felt totally devastated as she learned the consequences for her abilities as an artist and of limited treatment options. In losing her art, she felt she had lost herself.

Jocelyn contacted her only family member, her sister, Linda, although the two were never close. Linda responded to Jocelyn's news of her life-changing diagnosis with a nervous expression of sympathy. She did not offer to visit or to help in the long run. Jocelyn was deeply crushed at her sister's lack of support.

She felt that her life was over. She wouldn't be able to paint or teach, and there was no one to care for her or provide support. Overwhelmed by it all, she took a large overdose of pills. She was found by another teacher, who had been worried about her, and brought to the emergency department. She was admitted to hospital and recovered from the suicide attempt. A psychiatrist recognized that she was at risk of another overdose and needed follow-up.

During the hospitalization, she met a member of the spiritual care team, Fr. Tim, who knew her art. He encouraged her to express her greatest fears of the disease and listened carefully. He helped her understand that she had tried to end her life because of her fear that in losing her artistic abilities, she was losing herself. He helped her grieve that loss and the life it had promised. In his patient and quiet listening to her grief, anger and fear, he helped her understand that she was much more than an artist and was precious in herself.

Over the next several months, her disease slowly progressed. She became increasingly disabled and had to use a wheelchair, but was still able to drive. In schools with wheelchair access, she continued teaching in the classroom. In schools with stairs, she devised a unique art project. She asked the local telephone company to donate wooden telephone poles that were being replaced and supervised the children carving totem poles in the parking lot! This project was hugely popular with the students and the local community, and was a source of joy and pride for Jocelyn.

A group of teachers developed a community of support for her. They wanted her to understand her identity as an inspirational art teacher and friend. There were frequent hospitalizations through the year for flare-ups of her disease. By the end of the year, Jocelyn decided it was time to submit her resignation. She continued to function as an adviser for art projects. She had a particular rapport with special needs children, for whom she directed a wheelchair art program. By this time, she had befriended a number of the nurses and medical staff at her local hospital. She would sometimes take on the role of patient in the course on patient–doctor communication for health professional students. In this way, she was still teaching.

As her condition deteriorated, she kept in touch with Fr. Tim. He responded to her loss of identity and helped her understand deeper spiritual sources for her identity and self-worth.

LOSS OF IDENTITY IN PHYSICAL DECLINE AND DISFIGUREMENT

Loss of identity is a threat to all who experience losses due to serious and chronic illness or disability. Our physical appearance and strength can be profoundly altered; the talents and abilities which defined us and in which we took pride can be irretrievably lost; our role in our families, work and our communities unalterably compromised. We can feel that we are falling apart – literally disintegrating – and painfully experience what has been called an "identity crisis" (Erikson, 1959).

Jocelyn was diagnosed in young adulthood with a severe form of multiple sclerosis, a chronic, progressive and life-shortening neurologic disease. In a devastatingly short time, her life story has been radically transformed from an iconic success story of an independent and talented young woman to a tragedy. She experiences many serious symptoms, including spasticity and difficulty walking, joint contractures and sensory and vision loss. These changes alter profoundly her life and her art. She has to accept that there is no cure for her type of multiple sclerosis, though medications can help with many of her symptoms. We know that fatigue and depression are highly related to quality of life, which, in turn, is related to hopelessness and suicidal thoughts (Breitbart et al., 2000).

Jocelyn was helped by friends who developed a community of support and who stimulated her creative capabilities to find new ways to promote a love of art in students. Though not a formally religious person, she was attentive to spiritual realities. Fr. Tim provided her with some books he had on masterpieces of religious art. Jocelyn is totally captivated by the images in a way books have never worked for her. As she and Fr. Tim reflect on the fundamental vulnerability and strength captured in these works, she is helped to understand the deeper foundations for her identity as child of God and her personal inestimable worth, even in her experience of loss of physical capabilities.

GLORIA AND RICHARD'S STORY OF RELATIONAL IDENTITY IN DEMENTIA

Gloria, an 87-year-old wife, mother, grandmother and successful businesswoman, was diagnosed more than 16 years ago with vascular dementia and atypical Alzheimer's disease. She was a strong and independent woman who left Barbados at the age of 16 to train in England as a nurse before moving to Canada. There she met and married Richard, over 60 years ago. She founded a medical supply company and was recognized as the Business Person of the Year by her community. As a friend described her, Gloria was "a force of nature."

Her initial symptoms of headaches and confusion were written off as related to a serious car accident; Richard, who was having cardiac problems at the time, was Gloria's concern. She was still working at the family company but struggling to hide the fact that memory loss and confusion were making it impossible for her to cope with her responsibilities.

Gloria exercised and did crossword puzzles with Richard when she heard these activities might delay loss of memory. When she could no longer read, Richard read to her, and when she couldn't take her medications properly, her younger daughter developed a chart to follow. Her worried family conspired to get a companion for Gloria in the home, despite her objections, by telling her they needed a cleaning lady. The caregiver was told that she should play along.

Early on, Gloria exhibited inappropriate behaviour and would talk to strangers as if they were friends. She believed that she could fool people about her confusion and forgetfulness. When her older daughter tried to convince her she was wrong about the facts of an issue, Gloria became hurt and angry and said, "I'm still a person, you know."

As her condition deteriorated, Gloria would become paranoid and accuse others of theft. She accused Richard of infidelity, which was untrue and very distressing for him. She could become verbally and physically aggressive. One day, she became so violent that Richard and the caregiver ran out of the house and called 9-1-1. The police arrived and she was taken to hospital.

REDISCOVERING THE ART OF DYING

Richard was frantic – he could no longer cope. Then the medical staff made it clear that Gloria could not be safely discharged home. This relieved Richard of guilt for this decision. The family worked hard to find a facility with a special unit for Alzheimer's patients. They also provide Gloria with costly 24-hour private care.

Once Gloria was institutionalized, her world began to shrink dramatically. At first friends would visit, but as communication has become more difficult, only Richard, their children and grandchildren come. Her children ensure that Gloria's room is decorated for birthdays, anniversaries and holidays. They insist that every day, Gloria is to be dressed and well groomed in the fashionable clothes she loved. Richard visits Gloria almost every day, unless he is ill or takes a rare day to fly his model planes. He reads to Gloria and sometimes just sits with her. He takes her to the mall or the park and to church on Sundays.

Gloria has repeated bouts of pneumonia, when the doctors tell Richard that the end is near. Each time Gloria rallies physically, but her mental deterioration is severe. Despite this, she has flashes of recognition and responds to loving touch. Richard has arranged for his parish priest to provide a funeral service for Gloria, who is not a Catholic. He is relieved to ensure this important celebration of his beloved Gloria's life when the end comes.

DEMENTIA AND THE RELATIONAL CHALLENGES OF IDENTITY

The story of Gloria, Richard and their family is a tragic and touching example of the personal and familial challenges of loss of identity in dementia. It is tragic in the profound, ongoing grief and the progressively devastating losses Gloria experiences. It is a family tragedy in the stress of uncertainty regarding responding appropriately over a difficult and demanding journey. But it is deeply touching in its sharing of the experiences of love and faithful care of Gloria's family. Dementia raises a new awareness of the deep mystery of personal identity. Because Alzheimer's can last as long as 20 years from diagnosis, as we see with Gloria, it is at one and the same time a challenge to fidelity in care and a long goodbye where waves and blown kisses from the traveller cease long before the journey ends.

Some, trying to provide consolation to loved ones in the face of cognitive decline, failure of recognition, behavioural changes and paranoia in Alzheimer's, say to the family, "She is not the person she once was." Far from consoling them, this kind of thinking adds to their suffering.

Our culture insists that the human person is defined by rationality, autonomy and choice. Alzheimer's disease has assumed a special status in our time, embodying as it does weakness, dependence, indignity, irrationality and loss of identity. It has become more dreaded than cancer because it forces us to consider what it means to be human. The older we live, the likelier the risk of dementia. The aging of the developed nations of the world provides the context for an unprecedented number of affected elders. No wonder it is considered the disease of our century.

With early diagnosis, we have an increasing number of first-person accounts of early Alzheimer's disease in both illness narratives and journals. As with Gloria, these provide a clear sense of self and a desire to persevere in the face of memory loss and confusion (Beard, 2004). Information from caregiver accounts provides poignant and painful testimony of the experience of loved ones (Brown Coughlan, 1993). From these personal accounts and a wide range of research, we know much about the journey of dementia that is revealed in Gloria's story.

Dementia develops gradually; individuals identify a growing sense of something not being quite right. Over time there are lost keys, and forgetting to turn off the oven. Then there is usually an acute event that cannot be ignored, like getting lost in a familiar neighbourhood or, as with Gloria, being unable to manage her company's petty cash. By the time of diagnosis, some are very frustrated and angry at their handicaps and limits on their freedom such as the loss of their driver's licence. Others have a feeling of total devastation at the feared diagnosis, are profoundly worried about their impairments and recognize the consequences of their grim future. In this stage there are concerns with identity preservation. Individuals, like Gloria, develop strategies to manage public impressions, such as minimizing problems, trying harder and using humour about having a senior moment to deflect concern. They find tactics to help forgetfulness and confusion, such as lists and reminder notes.

There is then a slow, inexorable progression of debilitating symptoms, including failing to recognize loved ones, memory loss that disrupts ordinary life tasks and planning, confusion with time and place, communication difficulties, inexplicable rages and even hallucinations. As Gloria's family experienced, there is distress from confusion and communication difficulties and increasing tension between preserving skills and independence and faking it to cover up accumulating losses. This is a time for reappraisal and reconstruction of self-loss, uncertainty, awareness of difference, concern for loved ones and downgrading expectations (Pearce et al., 2002).

Family suffering increases with the loved one's depression, outbursts, difficult interactions and loss of civilizing inhibitions. They learn that persons with dementia find comfort in schedules, minimizing surprises, and positive and cheerful environments. Each family will respond differently, as will each member of the family. These differences, particularly when trying to honour the desire for home caregiving, can threaten the peace and integrity of the rest of the family.

In the final stages of the disease, individuals become apathetic and totally dependent but, like Gloria, can still respond to kindness and affection. Writing from personal experience of a mother with Alzheimer's disease, feminist philosopher-ethicist Françoise Baylis has provided insights into the relational nature of identity, as manifested through relationships and interactions grounded in memory, belonging and recognition. These three elements are crucial in all stages of dementia, but especially at the last (Baylis, 2017). Baylis reminds us that when a person has lost memories, we must remember for them; when they are isolated in their cognitive losses, we must include them in our lives and celebrations; and when they fail to recognize even their closest loved ones, we must recognize and acknowledge them.

Richard and Gloria's children demonstrate beautifully their relational duties in Gloria's decline. Their visits and inclusion of her in celebrations and their need to have her dressed in the fashionable clothes she loved are all recognition of who she is. Richard's loving fidelity and presence are his way of saying Gloria is still the love of his life and the beautiful woman he married.

SPIRITUAL AND THEOLOGICAL DIMENSIONS

Both Jocelyn and Gloria experienced profound challenges to their sense of self and to their identity. Caring responses to both women require both foundational beliefs regarding personhood and identity and practical expressions of relational identity.

In society, there are ongoing philosophical debates regarding our identity as persons. Some have a falsely dualistic anthropology that distinguishes human beings from human persons. Some believe that those who have lost their cognitive capacities are non-persons, raising many deep ethical issues (Hughes & Baldwin, 2006). These beliefs put those with dementia at great risk, particularly with the legalization of medically assisted death.

For Christians, our identity as persons is an ontological, essential concept. It is not a functional concept to be lost when our capacities fail. Some persons with early dementia focus on spiritual issues and meaning, identifying a new or heightened awareness of important issues in life (Post, 2000). A deepened spiritual sense and awareness of beliefs and rituals such as rosaries, hymns and candles can elicit responses well into the end-stage of the disease. Caregivers also rely on prayer. The longer the need for care goes on, the more they pray. For all of us, dementia is a reminder of our own weakness, vulnerability and interdependence.

The Old Testament contains some beautiful and consoling expressions of identity:

"Before I formed you in the womb I knew you, and before you were born I consecrated you..." (Jeremiah 1:5)

"I have called you by name, you are mine." (Isaiah 43:1)

This deeply intuitive understanding of belonging was echoed by Gloria at a time when she was not able to recognize her daughter but could look into her eyes and say, "You belong to me."

Christian belief in our interdependence as children of God, along with the importance of communion and community, challenges us to accept the deep relational challenges of respect and care for those with dementia and all cognitive decline.

QUESTIONS FOR REFLECTION

- Do you think Jesus had a crisis of identity during his Passion?

- If Jesus asked you, "Who do you say that I am?" how would you respond?

- When you reflect on Jocelyn's story, what insights would you bring to her care?

- What are the most powerful messages for you in Gloria and Richard's story?

- Have you experienced a loss of identity in your own life?

- What are the implications for our care of those who are gravely ill, have a serious disability or are living with dementia?

5

The Dimensions of Suffering: Jesus Falls Three Times

While there is no scriptural basis for the three falls of Christ during his journey to Calvary, the traditional Stations of the Cross intuitively recognized the threefold nature of human suffering: physical, psychological and emotional, and spiritual. During his Passion, Jesus experiences all of these forms of suffering in his scourging, abandonment, betrayal, loneliness, humiliation and contempt, knowing his loved ones suffer because he suffered, and seeing his life's work seemingly end in failure (Martin, 2014).

Falling is a powerful metaphor. We can fall in love, fall off a cliff or be knocked down. Falling evokes a visceral experience of having the ground shift from under us, plunging into a void with nothing to cling to. In the split seconds of a fall, we experience a terrifying loss of control; the consequences of a fall can be life altering. Patients become exhausted by pain, suffering and the experience of mounting losses. While individuals have different capacities for coping, these experiences can bring physical falls as well as a deeper, overwhelming and disorienting sensation of staggering or reeling on the constantly shifting ground of serious illness and dying.

Pain and other physical symptoms, psychological and emotional distress, and spiritual suffering are distinct realities. We often speak of medicine alleviating suffering. Does it address all of these? The distinctions and relationships between these three types of suffering, and the role of medical science and technology in providing technical answers to spiritual suffering, have only recently been the subject of serious reflection in medicine (Cassell, 1991).

Medicine's lack of attention to suffering can be traced to a worldview that separates mind and body, while rejecting the notion of the spiritual. Some sophisticated work has identified the distinction between neuro-cognitive suffering and agent-narrative suffering. Neuro-cognitive suffering has a direct causal relationship with a medical condition such as anxiety disorder, diagnosable depression, psychosis, chest pain, phantom limb pain, insomnia, bone pain, hallucinations and seizures. Medical and psychological interventions can often be of enormous help with this type of suffering. Agent-narrative suffering is experienced as fear, loneliness, existential angst, pitifulness, disgust, sadness, worthlessness, anger and loss of independence (Jansen & Sulmasy, 2002). Agent-narrative suffering is about deep spiritual issues of identity and meaning. It can occur in association with medical conditions, but is experienced in all aspects of life, even for the physically healthy and well.

There is no quick-fix medication or miracle procedure for spiritual suffering. As Saint Pope John Paul II has said,

> Suffering is something which is *still wider* than sickness, more complex and at the same time still more deeply rooted in humanity itself. A certain idea of this problem comes from the distinction between physical suffering and moral suffering ... *physical suffering*

is present when "the body is hurting" in some way, whereas *moral suffering* is "pain of the soul". (*Salvifici Doloris,* 1984, no. 5)

Suffering has been the subject of much theological and philosophical thought. As we see with Jesus in his Passion, suffering is experienced by the whole person, not just their body. Suffering occurs in many situations where there is no physical disease or impairment. Just think of the anguish of a mother whose child is lost to drugs and prostitution, or someone with survivor guilt after a horrific disaster. Meanwhile, many who have a serious illness or disability, and even those who are dying, can experience no significant suffering because they are at peace. Suffering is not an option in human life, and it is irreducibly unique and particular to the person. However, some common dynamics of suffering have been identified, including a profound sense of loneliness, isolation and marginalization, an experience of a disintegration of mind and body, a total loss of control and of "voice" (Kleinman, 1988). All of these dynamics need to be taken into account in the care and support of those who suffer.

Suffering is a mystery – not in the sense of a puzzle to be solved, but in the deeper sense of something not fully knowable. Suffering challenges us to drink the cup that Jesus drank: the cup of our own personal suffering, and the overflowing cup of the suffering of others.

5.1 Pain and physical suffering: Jesus falls the first time

In the first fall, the Christian imagination recognizes the sheer physical burden Jesus experienced in carrying a heavy, rough cross after an emotionally exhausting period of betrayal, imprisonment, judgment and physical abuse. Though he was a middle-aged man accustomed to hard physical labour and fatigue, tradition intuitively recognizes that, during his way to

Calvary, Jesus experienced the profound human vulnerability caused by pain. In this first fall, Jesus is weighed down with pain and can no longer rely on his physical strength to protect or sustain him. He needs help.

Joe's story and the price of pain

Joe, a widower and proud grandfather of three, is still a large man at 67 years of age. Over six foot two, with broad shoulders and powerful legs, he was a football star in his youth and a construction worker for over 40 years. Joe was a little loud and rough around the edges. All his life he had worked, played and lived hard. But he was described by all who knew him as a diamond in the rough who had a heart of gold.

A lifetime of manual labour and hard living had provided Joe with many experiences of pain. His approach to pain, like his approach to all difficulties in life, was to tough it out and not give in while nature healed the cause. This approach more or less worked for Joe until his wife, Francie's, sudden death after a car accident seven years ago. She was the love of his life and the gentle peace-making soul who helped soften and repair some of Joe's abrasive effects on family and friends.

The loss of Francie sent him spiralling into a deep pit of despair. He developed a very serious problem with alcohol and drugs, which nearly cost him his relationship with his son, Randy, and his beloved grandchildren, Sophie and Kendall. When he realized what was at stake if he kept on drinking, he worked hard to get sober. While in therapy, he learned much about himself and gained new insights about his response to pain and distress. He had drifted away from the faith of his childhood years ago, but rediscovered the power of faith and grace during his recovery. He had been doing well and was proud of the fact that he had overcome the drinking problem. He had a new-found hope that he now had a real chance to "make a lot of things right that I've done wrong."

But suddenly, things went horribly wrong for Joe. His back pain became so persistent and insistent that he could no longer ignore it or manage it with over-the-counter medications. Randy insisted he get medical attention. After extensive investigations, he was diagnosed with multiple myeloma, a cancer of the bone marrow. He managed a course of chemotherapy in hopes of getting more time, but it had taken its toll both physically and mentally.

Joe was living at home with home palliative care assistance. When asked, he replied that his pain was manageable. Yet the palliative care nurse realized that the hearty, outgoing Joe was becoming more preoccupied, immobile and hesitant. Any movement could cause a resurgence of pain that would lead him to wither and withdraw, his face reflecting fear. He is now reluctant to do anything that might cause pain, but is even more reluctant to talk about managing the pain better.

Randy was happy that his father had turned his life around. He visited with his children often. Joe was called "Grandpa Bear" by his adoring grandchildren because of his noisy, oversized hugs. On this visit, Joe was in great distress and he was just not himself; he was aloof with the children and avoided hugging them because of his pain.

The palliative care nurse visited just as the family left. She found Joe sitting on the side of his bed with uncharacteristic tears in his eyes. When she gently inquired about things, he said, "I hurt so much. I hurt all over. I don't know what hurts most, my body, my dying, or not being able to hug the kids." As the nurse again approached the issue of better management of his pain, Joe admitted for the first time that he wanted pain relief but was terrified about becoming addicted to painkillers because of his history of substance abuse.

Physical pain can shift the ground from under us and plunge us into suffering. Untreated or ineffectively treated pain is a major concern in the care of the seriously ill and dying. Unrelieved pain can interfere with the profoundly important spiritual and relational tasks at end of life. Assistance with pain control is the major reason for the referral of dying patients to palliative care services.

CRUSHED BY PAIN

Joe has been diagnosed with multiple myeloma, an incurable cancer of the plasma cells in the bone marrow. Bone pain, fatigue and an increased risk of pathological fractures are dominant symptoms in this disease. His pain has become overwhelming, but he is reluctant to discuss improved drug management. Because his pain is now interfering with his interaction with his family and his preparation for dying, caregivers need to understand his reluctance.

Pain is part of the human condition. All of us, at some point and for short or long periods of time, experience physical pain. Acute pain can serve as a warning to protect us from harm. Chronic pain has a corrosive effect and can surpass other symptoms of the underlying medical condition as a source of relentless suffering. We share common understandings *of* pain, but in reality, our experiences *with* pain are deeply personal. These understandings and experiences are filtered through the lens of our unique biology, personality and coping strategies as well as our family, community and society (Institute of Medicine, 2001). This means that our personal understanding of pain is shaped by our unique life story of health and illness. In turn, our life story shapes our experience of pain. Addressing Joe's pain effectively requires careful attention to physical, psychosocial and spiritual aspects (Thai & Fainsinger, 2011). Control of his pain depends on his understanding and his need, the availability of medical and pastoral expertise, and the support of his family. At the community level, it requires a meaningful commitment to improved pain education and palliative care services.

There are many reasons to manage Joe's pain more effectively. Pain can worsen depression, produce a paralyzing fatigue, hamper optimal functioning and diminish quality of life. As we are seeing with Joe, it can create stress and extract high psychological and relational costs in families. When pain is controlled, it is easier to cope with illness and deal with the inevitable losses and challenges at end of life.

While many today avoid pain at all costs and overuse pain medication, others, like Joe, will choose to bear different amounts of pain for many reasons. Pain can lead to the development of unexpected personal strengths and an astonishing resilience, but it is a fearsome way to develop such qualities. Some fear the sedating effects and want to remain as alert as possible for visits with loved ones or family special events, such as weddings or graduations. While this often presents difficulties for caregivers, who want to provide more comfort, the informed choices of competent patients must be respected.

As we saw in the stories of Hardeep and Colleen in Chapter 2, informed choice, which includes both consent and refusal, requires that the patient have the information they need to make a decision presented in a manner they can understand, the capacity or competency to judge the consequences of the information for them and their life story, and freedom from undue fear, influence and coercion. Joe's reluctance needs to be assessed through these criteria so that caregivers can support a freely chosen response to his pain, but also identify issues that may be limiting his free choice.

RESOURCES FOR PAIN MANAGEMENT

Joe needs to know that there are many available resources to manage his pain. Pain can be managed by a wide range of medications, including analgesics and opioids, steroids, muscle relaxants and cannabis. For cancer-associated bone pain, such as Joe has, biophosphates can help, and for nerve pain, anti-depressants and anticonvulsants are used. There are non-drug options, including radiation, relaxation therapy, physical and occupational therapy, and acupuncture. In refractory pain, local anesthetic nerve blocks may also be considered.

Moderate to severe pain responds to doses of opioid medications such as morphine, hydromorphone, fentanyl and oxycodone. There is a long history of using these medications for relief of pain and other symptoms with the goal of the fewest side effects at the lowest dose. Paradoxically, North Americans need to address inadequate pain control for many of the terminally ill and dying in the face of the increased use of prescription opioids to treat pain in general, and a major public health crisis of opioid and fentanyl misuse that is causing frightening numbers of deaths of adults and adolescents. The public health crisis is crucially important, but it presents a clear and present danger to effective pain management for the dying.

Many don't use medications for pain control because of some pervasive misinformation, such as the belief that doses used to control severe pain hasten the patient's death. When these medications are prescribed, the dose is carefully matched to the assessment of the symptoms. It can take hours or days to achieve symptom control, as the dose is increased gradually depending on the patient response. This carefully graduated approach does not hasten death (Portenoy et al., 2006). Another misunderstanding is that pain medications lose effectiveness over time and fail to control pain when things get really intolerable. There is no evidence to suggest that this happens. Doses may need to be increased over time, but this is due to increased severity of the symptoms. Treating pain helps people sleep, eat and move better, and these effects help them live longer, so there is no reason to save pain control for late in the course.

The issue of addiction to painkillers, which is a cause of concern for many, is of enormous personal significance to Joe. The large majority of terminally ill and dying patients can use these drugs without fear of addiction. It is a sad irony that patients facing death need not worry about a long life of addiction. The most significant risk factor for addiction is for those, like Joe, who have a history of substance abuse. He needs to know that he still deserves to have his pain controlled and that there are supports to help him do this in a healthy way.

As Joe considers his options, he and his family also need to know about the specific plan of pain management, anticipated side effects and how they will be addressed, and how effectiveness will be monitored. The capacity element of informed choice requires that Joe consider the consequences of his choices and their meaning for him and his wishes and values as he comes to the end of his life story. This includes considering the consequence of refusing pain management.

The final element in informed choice is freedom or voluntariness. This requirement recognizes that no one is completely free when making decisions in pain or distress, especially when faced with terminal illness and death. What is needed is sufficient freedom from undue fear, undue influence and coercion. As the health care team reviews Joe's history, they are deeply concerned about his fear of becoming addicted again and losing the opportunity for healing and reconciliation with his family. He says, "God gave me a last chance for a 'do-over'. I just can't blow it."

JOE'S LEGACY OF LOVE
AND RECONCILIATION

Joe is dying and he knows it. Just as he had turned his life around from a dark time and had begun reconciliation with his family, he was crushed again by cancer. He is terrified at the thought that he has very little time to repair the damage he has done. He is so fearful that acceptance of drugs will push him back into addiction and his bad behaviours that he is having difficulty making choices that could help him.

Joe's pain is interfering with his ability to deal with the four things that matter most when you are saying a final goodbye: "Please forgive me." "I forgive you." "Thank you." "I love you" (Byock, 2013). He feels a particular urgency to say all of these to his son, and a strong desire to leave his grandchildren a legacy of love. Joe's caregivers need to recognize and support him in dealing with the spiritual aspects of dying (Chochinov & Cann, 2005).

In his journey to recovery from alcohol and drug abuse, Joe learned to admit that he was powerless and needed to trust in God. His dying can be a time of grace for him and his loved ones. He needs to be assured of the importance of pain management as he writes the last chapter in his life story and leaves a legacy for Randy and the girls. Pain can not only crush the body, it can crush the soul and prevent prayer and interfere with relationships. Church teaching recognizes that appropriate pain management can serve as

> organic and psychic relief making prayer easier and enabling one to give oneself more generously ... help to make the course of the illness less dramatic and contribute to the humanization and acceptance of death. (Pontifical Council for Pastoral Assistance to Health Care Workers, 1995)

Joe has a lingering and unexpressed concern that his pain is deserved as a punishment for his sins. He needs to be reassured that Jesus dispelled the link between illness and sin in response to a question about the man born blind:

> As he walked along, he saw a man blind from birth. His disciples asked him, "Rabbi, who sinned, this man or his parents, that he was born blind?" Jesus answered, "Neither this man nor his parents sinned." (John 9:1-3)

Moreover, the Church has never taught that we are obliged to refuse pain medications as a means of purification or mortification. On the contrary, it recognizes that it is difficult to pray and prepare for death when you are constantly distracted with pain or other symptoms.

Joe recognizes that his loved ones suffer when they see him in pain, and this is not what he wants for them. He accepts his need for help. He has a full pain management assessment by the team and agrees to medication management. Over a short period of time, he feels significantly better. When Randy and the girls visit, he is more like his gruff but loving self. On this visit, eight-year-old Kendall was heard whispering to her sister, "Grandpa Bear is very sick, so his hugs are not as big but they are still the best ones ever." Joe is greatly comforted that this will be his legacy.

QUESTIONS FOR REFLECTION

- What might be the most important messages for Joe in the pain and suffering of Jesus, the innocent one?

- What are the features of Joe's story that touch you most?

- What would you want to say to him?

- Have you ever been crushed by pain?

- How do you deal with pain and physical suffering?

- How do you respond to the pain of others?

5.2 FALLING INTO DEPENDENCE AND PSYCHOLOGICAL SUFFERING: JESUS FALLS THE SECOND TIME:

The second fall recognizes Jesus' experience of psychological and emotional distress during his Passion. With this second fall compounding his pain and fatigue, he must have feared that he could not get up again, that it was hopeless to even try. This fall of Jesus represents the suffering in our mind and heart, which can often be hidden from others. It can be more distressing and debilitating than pain and other physical symptoms precisely because our psychological coping mechanisms themselves are directly affected. Fear, anxiety, uncertainty and loss of control can disorient and disable us, even more powerfully than pain and other physical symptoms can, especially when they are accompanied by clinical depression.

There are many examples of psychological and emotional distress for us and our loved ones in situations of illness, dependency and dying. Here, we reflect on a story of psychological and emotional suffering in the increasingly common personal experience of aging, physical and cognitive decline, and the social and health crisis of disrespectful and inappropriate care for our elders.

Jesus himself died in what was then middle age. A devout Jew, he was taught that aging was a gift and a divine blessing *"Grey hair is a crown of glory; it is gained in a righteous life"* (Proverbs 16:31). He learned the critical importance to the Jewish people of respect and honour for parents and other elders in the fourth commandment, which included the duty to care for them (Exodus 20:12).

Jesus knew well the central stories of Jewish history, which prominently featured the remarkable role of elders in salvation history (Moses, 2015). The Old Testament makes it very clear that the call to make a new covenant with God comes to Abraham and Sarah in their old age (Genesis 18:9-10). In fact, we are told they both laughed when informed that they would have many descendants. They were well beyond the age of bearing children and had accepted barrenness. But they were to learn that nothing is impossible for God! So this elderly couple trusts in God and Sarah delivers a son, Isaac, and founds the people of God. Later in salvation history, when the Jewish people are in captivity, it is Moses, who we are told explicitly was old, who was called to lead the Israelites out of Egypt and to the Promised Land – a journey that would last for 40 years (Exodus 6:10-13).

The Old Testament doesn't romanticize old age. It recognizes the vulnerability of aging in many of its stories and acknowledges that not all elders are saints. However, there is a clear and compelling vision that the elderly are called to continual responsiveness to God's call. From the weak and the barren, those society considers well past their prime, comes life abundant.

In Jesus' life we see this scriptural vision of the crucial role of older persons in salvation history. In the temple at his presentation to God, the elders praying there, Anna and Simeon, both recognize and announce Jesus (Luke 2:28-38). Elizabeth and Zechariah are old, and she is barren (Luke 1). Zechariah first doubts the promise of a son and is struck dumb for his disbelief. He and Elizabeth believe the promise and when all hope of a child was lost, Elizabeth bears John, who will proclaim Jesus as Lord.

Jesus also had an awareness and sensitivity to dependence in old age when he says to Peter,

> "… when you were younger, you used to fasten your own belt and to go wherever you wished. But when you grow old, you will stretch out your hands, and someone else will fasten a belt around you and take you where you do not wish to go." (John 21:18)

But Jesus does not see the elderly as beyond life and hope, for he tells Nicodemus that even an old man can be *"born from above"* in the Spirit (John 3:2-4).

Jesus, a good Jewish son, recognizes the vulnerability of a widow who is burying her only son.

When the Lord saw her, he had compassion for her and said to her, "Do not weep." Then he came forward and touched the bier, and the bearers stood still. And he said, "Young man, I say to you, rise!" The dead man sat up and began to speak, and Jesus gave him to his mother. (Luke 7:13-15)

He criticizes the Pharisees for teaching that a commitment to make offerings to God absolves one from the duty to care for aging parents (Mark 7:5-13), and tells the rich man he must honour his parents (Mark 10:17-19). One of his last acts on Calvary is to ensure that his own mother will be cared for after his death (John 19:26-27).

So, Jesus came from a culture that understood aging as a grace, valued elders as wisdom figures, and willingly accepted the duty of care for them in their old age. Are there lessons from his life for our care of the elderly?

GLADYS' STORY OF AGING AND PSYCHOLOGICAL SUFFERING

Gladys, a 75-year-old fiercely independent and private woman, lived alone in her own home since her retirement as executive assistant to a bank president. She has been a highly organized woman with a full social life and active participation in her local parish. She has coped with progressively painful arthritis for years, but now the pain has become unbearable. She has become unstable even with the assistance of a walker, and has great difficulty in getting to the second-floor bedroom and bathroom. She is frustrated by some visual problems that have required her to discontinue driving, which means losing touch with friends. She feels increasingly isolated and useless.

Her niece, Christy, the mother of three teens, helps as best she can, but the burden is getting heavier, even with private homecare help with cleaning and meals. Getting Gladys to the doctor's office, grocery store or church became a nightmare, because Christy was terrified her aunt would have a fall.

One fateful afternoon just before Christy is to take her for groceries, Gladys does have a fall. She is taken to hospital and diagnosed with a fractured hip. During her hospitalization, her general medical condition deteriorates and it becomes clear that she can no longer cope at home, even with support. She needs admission to a long-term care facility. Because of the long wait list, even with her financial resources, she is humiliated to learn that she is considered a problem, blocking a bed and preventing some really needy person from getting hospital care. She is transferred to the hospital's unit designed for persons awaiting placement. She is angry and vehemently opposed to the move.

After admission to a residential long-term care facility, Gladys is a totally different person. She finds her dependence devastating and demoralizing.

She is unkempt, sitting with curtains drawn, watching a mindless reality show. She hates the lack of privacy, especially in her need for help with personal hygiene. Because of her new location, her niece cannot visit as often as she did before. Gladys has lost contact with her church friends. She refuses to participate in facility events, and believes that the staff is insensitive and always too busy to help her or listen to her.

Everything is a bother, as her life is now useless and meaningless. Some days she can't even get out of bed. She wishes a stroke or heart attack would come along and end things, or maybe she should end it all. Her doctor prescribes antidepressant medications and re-assesses her pain management. He recognizes that her distress is rooted in deeper issues of meaning. Gladys begins to feel some improvement and she reconnects with her friends in her church women's group. Her former pastor visits and helps her understand her need to find meaning and purpose in her present situation.

AGING AND FALLING
INTO DEPENDENCE AND DESPAIR

Therefore lift your drooping hands and strengthen your weak knees... (Hebrews 12:12)

Gladys' story has two elements. The first is the personal tragedy of her physical fall and its devastating emotional and psychological consequences. The second is a morality tale of sorts, providing insights into our culture's valuing of elders and its understanding of the duty to respect and care for them. The elements are linked, and this linkage is becoming the focus of attention in aging societies, as seen in the popularity of Atul Gawande's *Being Mortal* (2014). Gladys' story presents significant challenges to us as individuals and societies.

As Gladys aged, she experienced inevitable limits and decline in function. She was trying to cope at home, but she could not do it alone. As her own friends aged, she, like so many elders, was increasingly dependent on her only close family member, Christy, for care and support (National Academies of Science, Engineering and Medicine, 2016). They had inadequate home and community support, especially for respite care. Christy, who had her own family to care for, was feeling the stress. Sometimes this stress tested the loving relationship she and her aunt had always shared.

Gladys was challenged by the crucial tasks of meaning making in aging, which include issues of identity, dignity, autonomy and dependence in care. Her life story was that of a highly competent, organized and independent woman who was always in charge and took care of the needs of others. In the seconds it took to fall and fracture her hip, her world is turned upside down and her life story is changed dramatically. She is now in need of help and no longer has control of her life, which she believes is now ended in any meaningful way. For the first time in her life, Gladys feels useless.

Gladys has experienced what medical specialists in aging call "frailty." Medically, frailty is a consequence of age-related decline in many body systems. It is a precarious state of just barely holding it all together. Frailty brings increased vulnerability to poor responses after a stressor event such as a fall, heart attack or urinary tract infection. Gladys was functioning at home, but with increasing assistance from others until her catastrophic fall. Then everything changed dramatically, and health care couldn't put Gladys back together again. The devastating consequence for Gladys is that now she can't go home again!

Instead, she has to be moved to the dreaded nursing home with its hints of failure and abandonment, even in good physical facilities (Cole, 1992). The rite of passage to a long-term care facility, with its implications of moving from independence to dependence, the loss of privacy and control in living with unchosen others, and challenges to freedom and autonomy, have conspired to create a crisis of meaning and purpose for her. The facility staff recognize this but are alarmed by her desire to "end it all." They inform Christy, who requests a medical assessment.

Fortunately, Gladys' physician recognizes that she has a treatable clinical depression, a not uncommon medical condition in these circumstances. The physician also recognizes that Gladys' emotional turmoil, and her despair and talk of "giving up" on life, were about deeper issues of identity, meaning and purpose. They are a cry for help and for attention to psychological and spiritual needs. In addressing "despair at the end of life" – hopelessness, depression, loss of meaning, suicidal thoughts and desire for hastened death, meaning-centred interventions have been shown to increase spiritual well-being and sense of meaning, and to decrease hopelessness and desire for death. We have learned much about factors that enhance hope, including connectedness, attainable goals, spiritual beliefs and practices, and promotion of courage, determination, serenity, lightheartedness, uplifting memories and affirmation of personal worth. We have also learned about factors that suppress hope, including uncontrolled pain, discomfort, abandonment and isolation, and devaluation of personhood (Coulehan, 2011).

How we respond individually and collectively to Gladys and to all elders will depend on how we value and respect them and their role in our youth-obsessed and productivity-focused society. Since movies and television shows function as a mirror of society's values, their portrayal of older people is informative. Some, like *Grumpy Old Men*, encourage negative stereotypes. Others, such as *On Golden Pond*, *Driving Miss Daisy*, *The Best Exotic Marigold Hotel* and *Quartet* sensitively portray some of the deep questions of meaning in aging and dependence.

Respecting our elders
and the duty of care

Historically, living into advanced old age was the exception. With improvements in social conditions and advances in medical science, population aging is accelerating rapidly worldwide, from 461 million persons older than 65 years in 2004 to an estimated 2 billion by 2050. North America is woefully unprepared for the unprecedented social and health needs and the preservation of dignity in later life (President's Council on Bioethics, 2005). Society's focus on acute high-technology and cure-oriented health care, to the detriment of the full continuum of support for health and well-being and lack of integration of health and social policies, especially regarding housing, is deeply problematic (Sloan, 2009). The high cost of health care for seniors, much of it inappropriate or ineffective, fuels ageism and catastrophic predictions of a tsunami of seniors taking care from the young and middle-aged. All this has occurred within the same decades as profound changes to family structure, work life and place of residence. These social changes complicate the ability of families to assist their elders and create a significant ethical crisis of care and home for the aging (Moody, 1992). No wonder Pope Francis has said,

> A people who does not take care of grandparents, who does not treat them well, has no future! Why does it have no future? Because such a people loses its memory and is torn from its roots. (Pope Francis, *Meeting of the Pope with the Elderly*, 28 Sept 2014)

Some elements of the crisis include inadequate home and community care support for aging in place at home, inadequate numbers of health professionals trained in care of the elderly, and insufficient appropriate facilities for long-term residential care, especially for care of seniors with serious and complex health care needs. Within long-term residential care, serious problems have been identified, including demoralized staff, inadequate staffing, high rates of illness and workplace injury, and increasing violence at all levels.

In times past, elders were wisdom figures. Today, we don't call them "elders" but "the elderly" or "the old," focusing on their age and the consequences of aging, not on their role and purpose. In 1999, the very elderly Saint Pope John Paul II, who had Parkinson's disease, wrote,

> Old age too has a proper role to play in this process of gradual maturing along the path to eternity. And this process of maturing cannot but benefit the larger society of which the elderly person is a part. ... To exclude the elderly is in a sense to deny the past, in which the present is firmly rooted, in the name of a modernity without memory. ... the signs of human frailty which are clearly connected with advanced age become a summons to the mutual dependence and indispensable solidarity which link the different generations, inasmuch as every person needs others and draws enrichment from the gifts and charisma of all. (*Letter to the Elderly*, 10 Jan 1999, no. 10)

In our time, it is not unusual for a grandfather to ask his 10-year-old granddaughter how to work the computer. Today, we Google the internet for answers to everything and get lots of facts at lightning speed. We can confuse facts with information, which requires a context for meaning, and conflate both facts and information with wisdom, which is the gift of knowing how to be and do in a respectful, compassionate and just way. Valuing the wisdom of elders can be difficult in our time (Jecker, 1992).

The early Church recognized the precarious state of the *almanah*, the widow, in biblical times. It created an "order of widows" to identify their needs, to find ways to overcome their social isolation and to develop strategies to allow them to remain contributing members of the community for as long as possible (Kaveny, 2005). We need to awaken the Christian community to its duty to elders like Gladys.

The epistles demonstrate great respect for elders and concern for the care of widows. But older persons are not seen as passive objects of concern. They are challenged to do good until their last breath. We need to stimulate the moral imagination to envision new ways of long-term care for the elderly, rooted in their identity as participating members in the mutuality, community and discipleship of the church. Catholic theologian Karl Rahner, at 80 years of age, proposed that "aging is a grace not given to all. It risks radical failure, if it is not accepted as a time to live fully until the end" (Rahner, 1981) and not just a fading away.

Gladys' story challenges us to provide environments of care and respect that promote aging as a time of great grace.

QUESTIONS FOR REFLECTION

- How might Jesus' experience of weakness and dependence be a source of consolation for Gladys?
- What emotions rise up in you when you hear Gladys' story?
- What are your own thoughts about your aging?
- How do you think our society values aging and the elderly?
- What would be the characteristics of support you would want if you needed assistance in care?
- What are the responsibilities of the faith and civic communities in care of the elderly?

5.3 FALLING OUT OF LOVE WITH GOD AND SPIRITUAL SUFFERING: JESUS FALLS THE THIRD TIME

"I am deeply grieved, even to death...." (Matthew 26:38)

This final fall recognizes the spiritual suffering of Jesus. In many ways, spiritual suffering, a kind of soul pain, is the worst. Physical pain and emotional and psychological distress from abandonment, betrayal, humiliation and seeing his loved ones suffer because of his condemnation have caused Jesus to suffer, but this is even worse.

This third time, it is almost impossible for Jesus to get up and continue. This suffering is rooted in Jesus' need to find meaning in the apparent failure of his mission, and in the temptation to despair that God is not with him in his time of need (Navone, 1984). His spiritual suffering is directly related to his faith and trust in God as his loving Father.

Spiritual suffering challenges us to find meaning in precisely those experiences where we feel we have fallen out of the arms of God and have lost any sense of God's care and protection. This fall from faith itself can be experienced in serious health care crises for ourselves and our loved ones because threats to life and health confront, in real time and space, the intrinsic, inevitable and ineradicably spiritual core of humanity. Here, we explore the spiritual suffering of a mother on the death of her son.

DEBBY'S LOSS OF HER BELOVED SON

Debby is a 32-year-old wife and mother. She lost her five-year-old son, Sean, without warning, to meningitis five months ago. She has been devastated since then by an utterly heartbreaking grief.

Debby cannot remember a time when she did not want to be a mother. As a child, her friends often wanted to play princess or movie star, but she always wanted to play house and be the mother. In her teen years, she loved to babysit the neighbours' children. Debby grew up in a devout Catholic family that actively participated in church activities. She met Jason, who was a church youth worker, at a diocesan summer camp. She could not believe finding a wonderful man who shared her values and dreams for a family. When they married, she felt that God was blessing her beyond her wildest dreams.

For three years she had difficulty conceiving. She and Jason prayed together for the gift of children. Finally, their prayers were answered and she had a beautiful, healthy baby boy, Sean. Life was perfect and revolved around this happy child.

Suddenly, her world came crashing down when Sean developed a fever and vomiting which seemed, at first, to be a minor flu. He rapidly became sicker, to the point of losing consciousness; Debby called 9-1-1. In a terrifying chaos, Sean was rushed by ambulance to the local children's hospital. In the emergency room, he was diagnosed with life-threatening meningitis and admitted to the intensive care unit. Debby and Jason were totally overwhelmed and felt helpless. Debby found it excruciatingly painful to see her beautiful boy covered with tubes and intravenous lines, but could not leave his side. She touched and kissed him, but was powerless to help and protect him. Sean's condition deteriorated rapidly as the infection spread throughout his small body despite the best medical efforts.

Debby and Jason clung to each other and prayed for a miracle. The doctors gently explained to them that things were grim and advised them to let the family

THE DIMENSIONS OF SUFFERING: JESUS FALLS THREE TIMES

know. Their parish priest came to anoint Sean and pray with them. Their beautiful boy, their precious gift from God, died 10 hours after being admitted to the hospital. Debby collapsed, crying out, "Why? Why?"

Family and church members helped plan the funeral, as both Debby and Jason were paralyzed with grief. The service was a blur, but Debby has nightmares of walking behind the small white casket. Her grief was profound. She had lost her son and her identity as a mother, and she had failed to protect her child. She distanced herself from Jason. She needed to talk constantly about Sean, but Jason found talking about him unbearable and lost himself in work.

Debby is wildly angry with God because he had answered all her prayers and then taken it all away. She is also worried that God is punishing her. She cannot go to church because of memories of the funeral. She has not only lost her beautiful son but her faith and trust in God as her loving Father. She is in her own private and painful hell.

THE DEATH OF A CHILD AND PARENTAL GRIEF

The death of a child is a heart-wrenching, world-shattering experience. While all grief carries unique pain, the death of a child goes against the natural order because parents are supposed to die before their children (Lantos, 2015). Historically, the death of children was common and inevitable, before the social and medical advances of the 20th century. While this is tragically still true in much of the world, the death of a child has become an uncommon event in our Western technologically developed world.

.... 103

Debby feels utterly broken. She has lost her precious Sean and the dreams for a long and happy life for him. She has lost her identity as a mother and more than a little of herself. Sean's death has shattered her planned life story with its clear purpose and meaning. Her grief is made worse because there was no preparation or time to say goodbye (Liben, 2011). She is disconnected from Jason because of their different ways of grieving. She is unable to sleep and feels a crushing depression.

Jason is overwhelmed by grief and a sense of failure as a father for not being able to protect Sean or comfort his wife. At his insistence, they visit their family doctor, who knows that treatment of clinical depression or sleep disorders can be important components in coping with the physical and psychological manifestations of grief. Their doctor recognizes that these interventions can provide a kind of emotional and spiritual analgesia but fail to address the deeper source of their suffering. He refers Debby and Jason to counselling professionals with expertise in bereavement care.

They receive help in dealing with the questions of meaning in Sean's death, in accepting their need to support one another in their shared grief, and in the crucial challenge of forging ongoing bonds with their beloved son. Debby and Jason participate in a recommended bereaved parents support group. The grief counselling and support of others, who know the devastation of the loss of a child, relieve some of their isolation. However, it becomes increasingly clear that, for Debby, there is a deeper spiritual suffering here.

SPIRITUAL SUFFERING

Dame Cicely Saunders, the founder of hospice palliative care, described the concept of "total pain" to include spiritual distress as well as physical, emotional and psychological suffering. Historically, the spiritual was inherent in an understanding of *health*, a word coming from the same roots as *wholeness* and *holiness*. The original notion of whole person care included care of mind, body and spirit. With the emergence of modern science, and the decline of religion in contemporary society, we have experienced an unhealthy dualism in separation of mind and body. There has been rejection of the spirit as a legitimate concern for health and well-being. This fragmentation is the total opposite of whole person care.

Today, we lack a common language for conversation about the spiritual. Spiritual suffering can be related to physical and psychological suffering, but is distinct from them both (Musgrave & McGettigan, 2010). A tour of the local bookstore dramatically demonstrates the enormous interest today in the notion of spirituality, which goes to show that you just can't keep a fundamental human reality down! Unfortunately, the concept is so vague and has so many different meanings today that it risks being trivialized or translated into medical or psychological terms. The interest is so great there is even a *Spirituality for Dummies* (Janis, 2008) that provides an overview of notions of spirituality, including a sense of general well-being, New Age values, appreciation for traditional religious values, in contrast to the physical and practical as well as the pursuit of ultimate reality. Some understand spirituality as an alternative to religion, as in the frequently heard expression "I am spiritual but not religious." A crucially important distinction relates to the nature of the transcendent and the holy. For religions, this is a Supreme Being, whom most of us call God.

Spiritual suffering is experienced by persons with understandings of spirituality spread across the entire spectrum of religious and philosophical belief (Chochinov & Cann, 2005). Three essential elements stand out in spiritual suffering:

1. a profound, personal crisis of meaning with fear, vulnerability and sense of loss of control;

2. a relational crisis with unwanted dependence, ruptures in established relationships, and a sense that normal networks of support no longer work; and

3. a rupture of community with isolation, marginalization and loss of familiar and nurturing roles (Sinclair et al., 2006).

Individuals will cope with tragedy and loss based on both their unique life experience and the influence of their spirituality.

Religious coping

Spirituality and religion are related notions, but they are conceptually different. Spirituality, referring to the way a person lives in relation to non-physical and material reality, is a broader concept than religion (Kearney & Mount, 2000). All religions are concerned with spirituality, but not all notions of spirituality in our world are religious (Lazenby et al., 214).

The three essential elements of religion are beliefs, rituals, practices and community (Pargament, 1997). Religious coping is about how we make use of these beliefs and practices to make sense of and respond to tragedy and loss. Individuals are more likely to turn to religion in crisis if religion mattered in life. In religious understanding, times of difficulty can be holy times, because they bring us in touch with the mystery of life and they force us to face limitations. They can also be dark nights of the soul. Positive religious coping, rooted in a secure relationship with a loving God, is helpful. Negative religious coping, focusing on guilt and punishment, is obstructive (Doka & Morgan, 1993).

Spiritual care

Debby's deepest suffering is spiritual, and her resources for understanding and coping are deeply religious. Spiritual care is no longer an integral part of health care of the sick, dying and bereaved. There has been lack of integration for many reasons, including difficulties in definition and lack of clear assessment and treatment models (Fitchett & Nolan, 2015). Encouragingly, new models of spiritual care have been developed, focusing on identifying spiritual distress and personal faith resources, obtaining a spiritual history that helps integrate spiritual and religious beliefs into a treatment plan and acknowledging the importance of presence and accompaniment of those in spiritual distress (Hart, 2011).

Any assessment of Debby's spiritual care needs must recognize the centrality of her faith in her suffering and its resolution. Debby's beliefs, practices, attitudes and values should orient her now. But Sean's death has made a mockery of her trust in God. She now has no sense of God's presence to comfort her. The only scripture quote she can think about is *"My God, my God, why have you forsaken me?"* (Matthew 27:46). This prayer of desolation in the face of the unbearable is appropriate, and Debby needs to cry it aloud. How can a loving God allow this? Why did he not protect her beautiful, innocent boy? These feelings are themselves the cause of crushing pain.

Spiritual care can help restore Debby's beliefs in God's love for her in light of Sean's death through presence and accompaniment, reconnecting her with her faith community, and fostering and responding to hard and deep questions and reflections. Pathways to healing can come from reading scripture, prayer and the sensitive support of the community.

Debby needs help from the scriptures themselves. Her pastor listens to her rage at God and her identification with Jesus' cry of abandonment. He gently reminds her that

"For God so loved the world that he gave his only Son, so that everyone who believes in him may not perish but may have eternal life." (John 3:16)

Then little children were being brought to him in order that he might lay his hands on them and pray. The disciples spoke sternly to those who brought them, but Jesus

said, "Let the little children come to me, and do not stop them; for it is to such as these that the kingdom of heaven belongs." (Matthew 19:13-14)

Debby should be encouraged and helped to pray in new ways: not just in saying prayers, but in meditation and contemplation of the meaning of all this. Mary, the Mother of Sorrows, knows well the death of a beloved son and can be a powerful source of strength and consolation for Debby.

It has been said that it takes a village to raise a child. It also takes a village to mourn one. Debby needs help to reconnect with the faith community, which has been so important to her and Jason and could help them now. It is crucial for well-meaning individuals to avoid platitudes and pious phrases that do not acknowledge Debby and Jason's overwhelming loss. These superficial comments only worsen their feeling that no one understands what they are going through.

In devastating situations, such as the loss of a child, there is a natural tendency to blame someone. Debby is blaming God. Until Sean's death, she saw God as the benevolent one who rewards the good when they pray to him. Sean was the ultimate gift to her. Well-meaning friends, telling her that Sean's death, after so short a life, is part of God's plan just heightens her sense of betrayal. Her inability to return to church probably has little to do with the funeral and more with her rage at a God who she now feels is inconsistent, arbitrary and even cruel.

Debby's grief and loss are profound. She requires medical and psychological help, but there can be attempts to move into therapy too early. Debby and Jason need to know that the journey will get more difficult before it gets better. They also need to know they are loved and supported by a community that shares their belief that death is not the end but a transition. Love endures.

Debby's greatest suffering is spiritual. Unless it is addressed, her loss of faith and trust in God may be lifelong. She will have lost not only her son, but her God and herself.

Questions for Reflection

- How can Jesus' experience of desolation provide support and consolation for Debby?

- What role is Debby's understanding of God playing in her suffering?

- What is your experience with loss in childhood?

- Did religious beliefs and practices play a role?

- What has been your deepest experience of spiritual suffering?

- How can the community of faith best support this couple?

6

PALLIATIVE CARE: SIMON OF CYRENE HELPS JESUS CARRY HIS CROSS

As they went out, they came upon a man from Cyrene named Simon; they compelled this man to carry [Jesus'] cross. (Matthew 27:32)

Jesus is well on the way to Golgotha, the place of his crucifixion and death, when Simon of Cyrene enters the story. Jesus was carrying the heavy cross, the instrument of his own death, after a time of intense emotional and spiritual distress and physical abuse. He has been betrayed, condemned, abandoned, mocked and scourged. The soldiers recognized the difficulty Jesus was experiencing in carrying the cross and enlisted a passerby, a stranger to Jesus, to help. Simon is identified as coming from the field and the father of Alexander and Rufus. Because he was forced to carry the cross on the eve of Passover Sabbath, scholars think he was probably not a Jew.

Jesus, who has spent his life helping others, most of whom were strangers, now becomes dependent on help from a stranger. The scriptures say that Simon does not volunteer to assist the struggling Jesus but is "*compelled*" and forced to help. It is unclear how willingly or reluctantly he took up the cross of Christ, and whether his attitude to being forced to help supported Jesus or added to his suffering. But it was clear to the soldiers that the weakened Jesus needed help to complete his journey, and none of the disciples seems to have been ready or able.

Throughout his ministry of healing, Jesus knew well the importance of giving and receiving help in weakness. A touching example is given in his cure of the sick man at the pool of Bethesda:

> *One man was there who had been ill for thirty-eight years. When Jesus saw him lying there and knew that he had been there a long time, he said to him, "Do you want to be made well?" The sick man answered him, "Sir, I have no one to put me into the pool when the water is stirred up; and while I am making my way, someone else steps down ahead of me." Jesus said to him, "Stand up, take your mat and walk." At once the man was made well, and he took up his mat and began to walk.* (John 5:5-9)

In Gethsemane, Jesus rejected a violent response to what was happening to him. He chose to accept what was to come "*in fulfillment of the Scriptures*" and so never became a victim but remained free to choose how to respond. While the soldiers just wanted to hurry things along and get this job done, Jesus humbly accepts help in order to fulfill his mission. He provides a powerful witness to our inherent interdependence, not to a rugged individualism that "toughs it out" when the going gets rough.

Today, the loss of independence is intolerable. Being free to choose and act as we desire is highly valued, and dependence on others is to be avoided at all costs. When circumstances force us to accept help, we often experience it as a humiliating weakness, or we feel guilty at being a burden to others. Experiences of serious and debilitating illness, disability and dying force us to recognize and to accept our essential human frailty and our irritating and glorious interdependence. Giving and receiving help are essential to our human flourishing. Jesus models acceptance of care and support. Simon is a metaphor for all health care professionals, who help us in the context of serious illness and dying today, particularly those with the special expertise of palliative care.

MARK'S STORY OF THE CROSS OF DEPENDENCE AND PALLIATIVE CARE

Mark, a 56-year-old happily married successful radio announcer, regarded by all who knew him as a workaholic and perfectionist, was diagnosed with amyotrophic lateral sclerosis (ALS) two years ago. His first symptom was slurred speech, which he attributed to fatigue. But it progressed, causing great anxiety for him because he earned his living by speaking clearly. When he developed some weakness in his legs, it was obvious something was wrong. His family physician, Dr. Carl, was alarmed when he saw Mark. After he listened to the history and did a physical examination, he recognized that he needed the expertise of a neurologist to confirm his dire diagnosis. He told Mark he was not sure what was going on and would refer him to a specialist.

After an intense period of sometimes frightening medical assessment, the neurologist told him he had ALS. Mark had an immediate and terrifying image of the brilliant scientist Stephen Hawking, with a ravaged shell of a body, in a wheelchair and able to communicate only with computer technology. He was overwhelmed and felt he was falling into a black hole. Judy, his wife of 32 years, was crushed. Mark heard nothing the doctor said after the diagnosis; he was determined to fight this terrible thing and focus on maintaining independence in his own home.

Within a year he was too weak to walk and needed support to sit up straight. Then he lost his voice and began to have trouble swallowing; he decided to have a feeding tube put in because he was fearful of choking but still wanted to eat. As the disease progressed, saliva would cause a humiliating drooling. When he had his first episode of pneumonia, Dr. Carl tried to talk to him about home hospice palliative care and his need to complete a "do not resuscitate" order. He felt his doctor was giving up on him and flatly refused, so Dr. Carl did not pursue it.

Mark was still able to write about his needs and tried to keep things light, making jokes about his new silent-film pantomimes for everyday needs, but he could see Judy's sadness and helplessness as he grew weaker. He felt increasingly guilty for needing her help.

He knew from high-profile legal cases that others with ALS had turned to physician-assisted death, which was legal in his jurisdiction. He felt trapped in his body and saw physician-assisted death as the only way to escape this horrible prison. He felt ambivalent about dying, and he loved his family. But increasingly he felt panicked, and ending it all seemed to be the only way out. Judy was terrified when he wrote that he was thinking about physician-assisted death. She contacted Dr. Carl. The doctor was well aware of Mark's dire situation and realized the overdue need for a comprehensive assessment of his medical management and a deeper understanding of his emotional and spiritual issues. This time the doctor carefully explained how he thought palliative care could help Mark and his wife. Mark agreed to a referral to the local palliative care team.

Mark has received a devastating diagnosis. ALS, also known as Lou Gehrig's disease, is a relatively rare neurodegenerative disease that is well known because of its prominence in the media and court cases requesting physician-assisted death. Mark received the diagnosis with immediate, vivid images of what it meant for him with its relentless progression of debilitating symptoms, including spasticity and inability to walk, problems with communication and secretions, feeding and breathing difficulties, and pain (Myers & Chakraborty, 2011).

Because ALS leaves a shattered shell of a body with awareness intact, it has become a dominant narrative of suffering at end of life. Not everyone with ALS believes it has robbed them of everything. Stephen Hawking continues to do major life work despite the disease. Similarly, Mitch Albom's *Tuesdays with Morrie* (Albom, 2002) is a powerful and touching story of a teacher who decides to use his experience as a teaching tool on what matters most in life. Finding the meaning and strength to continue contributing to others in the face of massive limitation requires spiritual and psychological strength and the tangible support of loved ones and the community.

Communicating this dire diagnosis is difficult and emotionally demanding, even for specialists who have experience with such conversations. Very difficult information had to be processed by Mark and Judy after they got over the initial shock. There are major decisions ahead, and goals of care to be set and revised. From the time of diagnosis, the emotional and psychological issues, including depression, mood swings and personality changes, and the deep spiritual needs to come should have been clearly discussed with Mark and Judy.

Living well in serious and terminal illness

Like Jesus, Mark needs all the help he and his family can get. Yet, when his doctor wants to talk to him about palliative care, he adamantly refuses. This is not surprising, as there is deep misunderstanding of palliative care. Some see palliative care as a death sentence and fear that if we speak of it, the seriously ill or dying person will lose hope – even if it is false hope for cure. Others fear abandonment in their most vulnerable time, particularly when palliative care is presented as what medicine does when "there is nothing else we can do." Some even confuse acceptance of dying and a choice of palliative goals of care as equivalent to suicide or euthanasia. So it is not surprising that some palliative care professionals have even suggested changing the name of palliative care to supportive care, hoping to integrate the palliative approach into all serious, chronic, life-threatening and life-altering illness (Caprio, 2016). Unfortunately, Mark's doctor unintentionally feeds into these misunderstandings when he initiates conversation about palliative care at the same time as he raises the issue of "do not resuscitate" orders in the case of a cardiac arrest.

In the1960s, palliative care began in the hospice movement of Dame Cicely Saunders in the United Kingdom. Initially developed in response to poor symptom management and the abandonment of cancer patients when surgery, chemotherapy and radiation failed, hospice palliative medicine now encompasses care for all serious, life-altering and life-threatening diseases for all ages. Dame Saunders did not intend to develop a specialty area of medicine. She desired a revolution in all of modern medicine to return to whole person care and tame the dominance of medical technology (Saunders, 1981). The philosophy and goals of palliative care have been clearly articulated:

> Palliative care is an approach that improves the quality of life of patients and their families facing the problems associated with life-threatening illness, through the prevention and relief of suffering by means of early identification and impeccable assessment and treat-

ment of pain and other problems, physical, psycho-social, and spiritual. (World Health Organization)

While ALS is a devastating and complex disease, palliative care can be a powerful source of care and support for Mark and his loved ones. Ideally, Mark would have been offered a *palliative approach,* which balances effective medical treatment, aimed at pain and symptom control, with attention to psychosocial, familial and spiritual issues from the time of the devastating diagnosis.

Palliative care's key principles affirm life and regard dying as a profoundly important and normal human process, not a medical condition. Palliative care's foundational principles clearly indicate that it does not hasten death or prolong dying. Its goal is to help people to live as well as they can until they die. Far from abandoning patients and their loved ones, it is, as Ira Byock has eloquently stated, "the best care possible" (Byock, 2013). Palliative medicine can use highly sophisticated medical and surgical interventions for pain and symptom control in complex cases. It always aims to balance these interventions with care of the whole person.

Whole person care of body, mind and spirit requires recognition that pain and other physical symptoms are crucially important but distinct from suffering. In Chapter 5, we explored these distinctions through the stories of Joe, Gladys and Debby. Relieving the stress of pain and other physical symptoms allows patients like Mark to address psychological and spiritual suffering due to the multiple losses from serious illness and a life that is now limited. However, there is no medical prescription or procedure to cure suffering, which is a total, emotional and spiritual experience. It requires attention to the deeper issues of meaning in dependence and at end of life.

Despite demonstrated efficacy of palliative care in improving the quality of life of seriously ill and dying patients and family satisfaction with the care given to loved ones

(Steinhauser et al., 2000), it is still offered late in an illness or not at all. When Mark was first offered palliative care, he was focused on living and was not ready to discuss the limits of medicine or his inevitable decline and dependence. Because palliative care was not presented well from the beginning, it did not appear to be helpful to Mark.

Palliative care is a philosophy of care. It can be provided in the patient's home, hospitals, residential and nursing care facilities, hospices, and even on the street for homeless and marginalized patients. Every physician should have basic skills in palliative care, including competence in pain and symptom control and in discussing the changing goals of care. All physicians should know, as Dr. Carl did, that many seriously ill and dependent individuals, like Mark, will express thoughts about assisted death. They will also recognize when to seek specialized palliative care expertise in difficult and complex cases. Ideally, this full-service palliative care is provided by an inter-professional team made up of nurses, physicians, spiritual care providers, social workers, physiotherapists, occupational therapists and pharmacists. The team assists with the assessment and management of difficult symptoms, and then returns the patient to their home, if adequate support is available.

END-OF-LIFE HOSPICE PALLIATIVE CARE

Hospice palliative care helps patients like Mark to live as well as they can. Mark is not yet actively dying, but knowledge of what support could be available for him and his loved ones at the end is important. A crucial time will come when the focus is more immediate attention to preparing for the inevitability of dying. Medical advances have brought great advances to many, but unbounded belief in technology can make it difficult to recognize when the technology is simply prolonging dying rather than prolonging living. Patients, families and caregivers have identified what they think is important in end-of-life care. These include pain and symptom management, respectful involvement in decisions about treatment preferences, opportunities for achieving crucially the important personal and spiritual bucket list of farewells, reconciliation, giving and receiving forgiveness, and expressions of love and gratitude (Steinhauser et al., 2000). These are the elements of whole person care and the focus of end-of-life palliative care.

Most patients desire to die at home, but this is not always possible, especially as the end nears and the care becomes complex or too burdensome for loved ones. There are fail-safe options where patients can receive end-of-life care in a palliative care unit or in a hospice, a home-like setting that provides care in the last months of life. Unfortunately, hospice palliative services are not available to all, creating a crisis of justice and compassion for our care of the dying (Jennings et al., 2005).

For those who are concerned that choosing hospice palliative care at end of life is equivalent to assisted suicide and euthanasia, Pope Francis has affirmed that palliative care is compatible with the Christian notion of the *good death*, saying,

> Palliative care is an expression of the properly human attitude of taking care of one another, especially of those who suffer. It bears witness that the human person is always precious, even if marked by age and sickness. … The human person, in fact, in whatever circumstance, is a good in and of himself and for others, and is loved by God. For this reason, when life becomes very fragile and the end of the earthly existence approaches, we feel the responsibility to assist and accompany the person in the best way. (Pope Francis, *Address to the Pontifical Academy of Life*, 5 March 2015)

Dr. Carl consults the specialized hospice palliative care team. A comprehensive assessment uncovers Mark's well-hidden lifelong anxiety, which is unmasked by his illness. It is greatly reduced with proper medication. They find that Mark has some shortness of breath, and that his problem with excess secretions that cause drooling can be treated. The shortness of breath is managed with opioids. Medications are given to dry up his mouth at night and he is given a portable suction machine that he can use during the day. Within a few weeks, Mark is feeling less anxious and more comfortable physically. He has a greater sense of control now and is even able to manage a few visits with close friends, something he has been avoiding for months. While not a religious man, he begins to feel the need for spiritual support in finding meaning in all of this. He agrees to a visit from a priest friend of his wife's, saying, "It can't hurt to try!"

RESPONDING TO THOUGHTS OF ASSISTED DEATH

Dr. Carl recognizes many of the identified triggers to initiate serious end-of-life discussions in patients with ALS. He sees that thoughts of assisted death are a cry for help. Any physician who has cared for seriously ill and dying patients has had the experience of patients asking, "Can't you do something?"

He responds to Mark without judgment and with great care and compassion. First, he ensures a review of Mark's medical management and symptom control. He takes care to assess for the possibility of a clinically treatable depression affecting Mark's thinking (Breitbart et al., 2000). Then he sits down and takes the time to listen to the suffering that lies behind Mark's thinking about physician-assisted death. He does not immediately move into a legal assessment of Mark's eligibility for assisted death, but responds respectfully and empathetically to Mark's feelings and fears. Dr. Carl is well aware that the long-standing prohibition of Hippocratic, allopathic medicine against the intentional ending of a patient's life, even at their request, is no longer a foundation of modern medicine.

Dr. Carl is a practising Catholic. He accepts Church teaching that "Whatever its motives and means, direct euthanasia consists in putting an end to the lives of handicapped, sick or dying persons. It is morally unacceptable" (*Catechism of the Catholic Church*, no. 2277). He cannot, in good conscience, participate in physician-assisted death. He feels a deep obligation to Mark and does not want to abandon him. The help provided to Mark and Judy has shifted Mark's thinking for now. He is no longer thinking seriously about pursuing assisted death, but he is painfully aware that there will be difficult days ahead before he dies. Dr. Carl continues to care for Mark, but they both know now that a time may come when that becomes complicated and Dr. Carl will need to transfer care if Mark pursues assisted death.

LESSONS FROM THE CROSS

Simon was conscripted to carry the cross. He did not plan to help, but his plans were interrupted when the soldiers tagged him to help. Carrying a cross was difficult and shameful, as he shared in guilt by association. Simon was a stranger to Jesus, but he is diverted from his own journey and becomes involved in Jesus' suffering and in his mission of salvation. Rolheiser notes that Simon, this unimportant figure who just happened to be there and was forced to provide unglamorous service to Jesus, does the most important thing that will ever happen in his life and comes down to us as a sign of support in need (Rolheiser, 2015).

Mark's dying can be a precious time of grace, reconciliation and healing for him and his whole family. Health care workers, especially those in hospice palliative care, can bear witness to suffering and assist others in making their cross a little easier to bear. In reality, hospice palliative care can provide no guarantee of a death totally free from physical distress or emotional, psychological and spiritual suffering precisely because of its recognition of inherent limits and because of its commitment to whole person care (Curlin, 2015). It can relieve physical symptoms of pain and distress and provide a safe space where suffering can be transformed into emotional and spiritual growth. Palliative care does not provide *cure* for serious and terminal illness, but can provide a space for *healing* of the whole person and for a *good death.*

QUESTIONS FOR REFLECTION

- What do you feel when you think of Simon being forced to help Jesus carry his cross? How do you think Jesus felt?

- What touches you most in Mark's story?

- How do you respond to the offer of help?

- How do you respond to interruptions when forced by circumstances to help others?

- When and where are you called to be Simon of Cyrene today?

7

THE ART OF DYING:
JESUS IS CRUCIFIED

It was nine o'clock in the morning when they crucified him. (Mark 15:25)

The sign of the cross is the universally recognized devotional practice for Christians. It begins all of our prayer, our baptism into the faith and our committal of our loved ones to the grave. Nailed to the cross and in great pain, Jesus has apparently lost all control over his own life. So the cross could be read as a sign of failure and disgrace. Scripture and tradition read the sign very differently. The dying Jesus is not a passive victim, but one who is actively living out his mission to his last breath. Jesus' life of preaching and healing are important elements in his ministry, but it is during his crucifixion that he is most actively redeeming the world as he surrenders completely to the will of the Father. The medium is indeed the message, as Marshall McLuhan famously said.

Dying is a process that ends in the event of death. Jesus' period of dying was short in terms of hours, but he actively used that time to complete his mission. Jesus' mission is captured in his last words from the cross (Rosica, 2017). These words provide the text for the climax of Jesus' life story and allow us to read the true meaning of the cross and of our signing ourselves with this cross. They also witness to our belief that dying is a free, active, final ratification of life and not merely a passive process of decline (Rahner, 1965).

FORGIVENESS

When they came to the place that is called The Skull, they crucified Jesus there with the criminals, one on his right and one on his left. Then Jesus said, "Father, forgive them; for they do not know what they are doing." (Luke 23:33-34)

In his life, Jesus taught his disciples to respond to violence with mercy and forgiveness. In fact, those who crucified him knew exactly what they were doing in putting an innocent man to death. The deeper meaning here is that they do not know how much God loves them (Rolheiser, 2015). On the cross and actively dying, he lives what he taught, even to the point of forgiveness for those who betray and crucify him. His first words dramatically demonstrate the unlimited power of the love and mercy of God.

RECONCILIATION AND COMMUNION

[Jesus] replied, "Truly I tell you, today you will be with me in Paradise." (Luke 23:43)

Along with soldiers jeering at the foot of the cross, one of the criminals crucified with Jesus gets a false sense of courage and superiority and joins in mocking him. The other criminal, in a remarkable manifestation of faith and true courage, cries out, protesting Jesus' innocence. He acknowledges his own guilt and only asks to be remembered. Jesus, from his position of pain, responds with the extraordinary promise that "*today*" the repentant thief, who has likely been an outcast his whole life, will be in the company of Jesus in paradise forever.

THE DUTY OF CARE

When Jesus saw his mother and the disciple whom he loved standing beside her, he said to his mother, "Woman, here is your son." Then he said to the disciple, "Here is your mother." And from that hour the disciple took her into his own home. (John 19:26-27)

Mary accompanies Jesus at a distance throughout his ordeal. Imagine the indescribable pain of both Jesus and his mother! Mary, who said the great *yes* to God, ponders the meaning of what is happening to her beloved son. She remains faithful even when there are no easy answers, and she brings the gift of her presence. Jesus, a good and loving son, feels her sorrow. He knows what his loss will mean for her. He ensures that his mother will be cared for after he is gone. This is his final gift to her.

PRAYER OUT OF THE DEPTHS

"My God, my God, why have you forsaken me?" (Matthew 27:46)

In sharp contrast to the first three words of Jesus, which are all concerned with the care of others, and after hours of hanging on the cross, there is a darkness that descends on the land and in Jesus' soul. He experiences the profound isolation and loneliness that are frightening experiences in dying. His sense of failure in achieving the conversion of Israel is compounded by a sense that the Father has failed to protect him (Navone, 1984). In his anguish he cries out his feelings of abandonment even by the Father. His prayer to "*Abba*", the intimate name for "father" that Jesus used in Gethsemane, is replaced here with a scream from a forlorn Jesus to *"Eloi, eloi,"* the language not of a son but of a humble servant. Some scholars believe that Jesus is quoting here from Psalm 22 as an expression of hope, not abandonment, because the end of the Psalm is *"He did not hide his face from me, but heard when I cried to him"* (Psalm 22:24). But Jesus could feel abandoned by God.

Chicago Cardinal Joseph Bernadin expressed his own experience of this isolation when he was dying of cancer:

The essential mystery of the cross is that it gives rise to a certain kind of loneliness, an inability to see clearly how things are unfolding, an inability to see that, ultimately, all things will work for our good, and that we are, indeed, not alone. (Bernadin, 1997)

HUMAN AND SPIRITUAL VULNERABILITY

"I am thirsty." (John 19:28)

Jesus has experienced a difficult journey to the cross. The imprisonment, scourging, and crowning with thorns are all taking a tremendous physical toll. After hours on the cross Jesus is dehydrated and going into shock, but this is his only reference to his physical distress. When he cries out with thirst, he is offered the sour wine that was a common drink for the poor (Brown, 1994). The themes of water and thirst recur often in Jesus' life and ministry. Jesus asks for water from the Samaritan woman (John 4:13-14) not just because of physical thirst, but also because of a thirst for souls: a thirst for justice, compassion and the reign of God.

FIDELITY

"It is finished." (John 19:30)

Jesus has been obedient and faithful to the Father. As death approaches, he recognizes that his mission is complete and his suffering is coming to an end. Through this faithfulness, Jesus becomes the source of new life for us all.

FAITH AND TRUST

"Father, into your hands I commend my spirit." (Luke 23:46)

Jesus' final word is a prayer to the Father. In his life and in his dying, it is his relationship of utter and complete trust in the Father that impels and sustains him.

We hold the last words of our loved ones as special and to be treasured. This is true for Jesus' own last words. Throughout his time of dying, Jesus was not passive but continuing to fulfill his role in our salvation. His final words allow us to read the sign of the cross not as a sign of failure, but as the clear and compelling sign of God's unconditional love for us: "*For God so loved the world that he gave his only Son*" (John 3:16).

THE ART OF DYING

Jesus witnesses to dying as a deeply personal and transformative act that both ends earthly life and fulfills it. Today, we are scared to death of dying. In our Western technologically developed societies, we have little experience of dying. It is hidden away in hospitals and chronic care facilities and we don't know how to do it (Dugdale, 2015). It is no longer a natural, personal, family and community event, but is understood as a failure of medical science and technology (Nuland, 1994).

The role of the dying person has been replaced by the role of the patient needing care. The focus has shifted from assisting the dying with their role and in the difficult art of writing the final chapter in their life story to the role of the patient in need of medications and procedures. Art includes both great masterpieces of professional artists and the more modest works of craftsmen. All art combines skill and technique with inspiration and vision, so it must be practised and honed. The art of dying is not like work with clay or canvas where the artist can repair a failed attempt, but like the sculptor's chiselling away a piece that can never be put back again.

Modern research has identified three roles for the dying person: the practical and concrete tasks of preparation for death, relational engagement with others, and personal growth to the very end of their unique life story (Emanuel et al., 2007). The sense of a role here is not in the sense of a script to memorize, but more in the sense of both cultural and inherent personal understandings that provide normative guidance in fulfilling well the tasks at end of life.

The last words of Jesus witness to his practice of the art of dying in his attention to the practical task of assuring care for his mother; continuation of his relational tasks of love, healing and forgiveness; and prayerful fidelity to the Father's will until the last breath. Preparing for and accepting these roles in our own dying and in our accompaniment and support of our dying loved ones are crucial in an art of dying today.

ISOBEL'S STORY
AND THE ROLE OF THE DYING

Isobel is an 80-year-old Italian woman with four children and 12 grandchildren. Family has always been the focus of her life: celebrations are large and lively events, with Isobel happily preparing food for days in advance. Until recently, she and her 83-year-old husband, George, hosted these events. Isobel is always the centre of attention, telling stories of the old country, and encouraging all to "Eat, eat!"

Isobel has had two short hospitalizations for congestive heart failure over the past year. Despite her indomitable spirit, each episode has taken a toll on her and she is feeling weaker by the day. Her life had become dominated by tests and visits to the cardiologist, who was trying to find the right drugs to boost her failing heart. She prayed fervently for things to improve.

When she had a stroke, she lost her ability to speak clearly and developed difficulty swallowing, which required a feeding tube. Isobel and her family were devastated. George was constantly at her bedside, even when other family took turns to be with her. They prayed for a miraculous recovery and had prayers offered for her in her parish church. When Isobel's condition stabilized and she was discharged to a rehabilitation facility, George exclaimed, "Our prayers have been answered! I knew she would make it."

After weeks of rehabilitation, which was slow-going and demanding, in large part because of her failing heart, Isobel was able to speak with some difficulty. Her swallowing improved and the feeding tube was removed. Her family rejoiced that Mamma was on the road to recovery, and they cooked food for every meal so she would get strong again. Isobel knew she was far from recovery, but showed a brave face for her family. During her time in rehab, she felt a strong need to have one of her grandchildren help her write down her secret recipes and stories of growing up in Italy. She also had George contact an estranged sister who came to visit after years of separation.

Isobel then had a series of small strokes and was confined to bed. She was comforted when her parish priest visited and provided the sacrament of the sick, though one of her sons protested that "these are not the last rites." She tried to have a conversation with her eldest son about care for George, but he avoided it. Isobel was clearly failing now; her congestive failure worsened and she developed pneumonia, which required admission to the intensive care unit. Despite aggressive treatment, the lung infection spread through her body. The doctor tried to raise the question of goals of care with Isobel and her hopes and wishes for the end. Weak now, she told him, "I'm just tired out. I think it is my time now." George and her children, who were present, refused to listen and begged her, "Don't talk like that. Just try to eat, because we need you." Isobel replied that she was doing her best but was just not hungry.

The family demanded that the feeding tube be re-inserted. Isobel's physician tried to explain that she was dying and her lack of appetite was normal. He reassured them that she could still eat and have sips of favourite drinks if she wanted. A feeding tube would not help now and could overload her body with fluid and be harmful. Isobel's family was very angry at this situation. "Surely you can't expect us to let our Mamma die of starvation and thirst. We love her and have to feed her. It's our duty. We are praying for another miracle."

DYING AS A TIME OF GRACE

With some difficulty, Isobel has come to accept that she is dying. Her acceptance should allow her the precious grace of time for completing the last things of life: farewells, forgiveness, expressions of love and gratitude, and reconciliation. She is intuitively trying to fulfill the practical and concrete tasks of preparation for death, including ensuring care for George, engagement with her family in handing on recipes and stories as signs of love, and faithfulness to her God. She needs the help and support of her family, but their struggle to accept her dying is an obstacle for her. Isobel's family is grieving and denying what is happening. Rather than cherishing this precious time together, they are focusing on feeding her to restore health, and on hope for a miracle cure. Their grief is manifested by anger and frustration.

Being able to leave loved ones when we are dying and giving permission to loved ones to go are crucial. Isobel's family could be a critically important source of care and support for her in her dying. They need help to give her permission to go, and she needs their permission to leave them.

Food and drink at end of life

Food and drink give life to the body. Food and drink shared give life to the mind and spirit, and through them we celebrate our communion with friends and family. Providing food and drink is filled with deep meaning. Preparing food for others is a sign of our love and caring. Enjoying the food is a way of accepting love and showing gratitude and respect. For Catholics, there is even a holy, sacramental significance to shared meals, because the celebration of the Sunday Eucharist is the great meal where the family of faith comes together to give thanks and to feed the soul.

Isobel's family urges, nags and pleads with her to eat because this signifies their care for her. Lack of appetite is a normal part of dying; since meals occur several times each day, they are frequent, painful reminders that the loved one is coming to the end of their life. Because of the emotional and spiritual importance of food and drink, a loved one's failure to eat can be a source of anxiety, grief, anger and guilt for them and their loved ones. These feelings are compounded by misunderstanding and myths surrounding food and drink in dying, particularly about loved ones "starving to death" or dying of thirst, and the presumed benefits of assisted nutrition and hydration in dying (Shannon & Walter, 2005).

Isobel's family believes improved nutrition will strengthen her and aid recovery. Despite evidence to the contrary, they think it will make her more comfortable and prevent her from dying from starvation or dehydration (Ganzini, 2006). Thirst causes distress because it causes a dry mouth. When Jesus was dying and said "I am thirsty", he was given a sip of common wine on a sponge to wet his mouth, just as we do when we lovingly wipe the dried lips of a dying person with a moistened sponge.

Failure to eat results in weakness and fatigue rather than acute hunger pangs. A feeding tube is helpful when someone is temporarily unable to eat. It was used to provide Isobel with nourishment as she was recovering from her stroke. Now that she is actively dying, a feeding tube will not change the outcome. Indeed, it carries the risk of distressing complications, including pain, infection and bowel perforation.

We hunger and thirst for more than food and drink. The family needs to be reassured that a small amount of her grandmother's lasagna or a sip of her favourite wine can still be shared with Isobel as a sign of love and care. The focus is on the taste, the smell and the memories that the food brings, not on its nutritional value. Providing food or fluids beyond what Isobel asks for will not contribute to her comfort or prolong her life.

WAITING FOR A MIRACLE

Isobel and her family are devout Catholics. Prayer is important to them and has sustained them through Isobel's decline in health. The gospels are filled with stories of God's miraculous power manifested through Jesus' cures. But here, the family is using hope for a cure to avoid facing the reality of Isobel's dying. They are focusing on the God who rescues and limiting God's action in Isobel's life to what they desire as an outcome. They are failing to acknowledge, as we have seen in Jesus' dying, that God is also the one who empowers the dying to face death with courage and hope. In their grief, they are trying to limit the mystery of God. There was no miraculous rescue of Jesus from death, but amazingly and against all human logic, God's greatest miracle is that death does not have the final word. Resurrection triumphs over death.

Isobel feels the need for God's love and support as she accepts her dying. She also needs the support of her caregivers and of pastoral care. She desperately needs her family to support her. Her family urgently needs caregivers willing to listen to their concerns and to journey with them in their grief, but also to help them understand that their beloved Isobel is dying. Pastoral care can help them to grasp the important role they play in supporting Isobel in this precious time of dying. They need to be gently reminded that attempts to cling to biological life at all costs are a contradiction of their fundamental belief in the power of the resurrection. They need to trust that even in their deep loss, the Lord "*will wipe every tear from their eyes. Death will be no more; mourning and crying and pain will be no more*" (Revelation 21:4).

QUESTIONS FOR REFLECTION

- How do you respond to the last words of Jesus, aware that he spoke them in the agony of his crucifixion?

- How do you read the sign of the cross?

- What do you find most compelling in Isobel's story? What is most challenging?

- What is your most powerful experience of loss of a loved one? What role did you play in supporting and comforting them as they were dying?

- When you think about your own dying, what feelings surface? What role does faith play in your attitude towards dying?

- If you were diagnosed with a terminal illness, what would be most important for you? What use would you make of your time?

8

FAITHFUL TO THE END: JESUS DIES

Then Jesus gave a loud cry and breathed his last. (Mark 15:37)

"Father, into your hands I commend my spirit." Having said this, he breathed his last. (Luke 23:46)

Jesus' period of dying is depicted in scripture in great detail, especially in the presentation of his last words. His moment of death, after several hours on the cross, is described in surprisingly stark language. In contrast to graphic depictions in art and movies, including Mel Gibson's 2004 film *The Passion of the Christ*, little attention is paid to his physical death. After a prayer to the Father and a loud cry, which in the original Aramaic, *eboesen,* can mean not only a shout but an intense scream (Brown, 1994), Jesus stops breathing. An intense and anguished cry, a prayer, and then comes the moment of Jesus' death.

The scriptures provide few details about the crucifixion itself, because early Christians knew it well. Victims of crucifixion died from a combination of blood loss, dehydration and asphyxiation, because the weight of the body made it difficult to expand the lungs. Pilate wants to have the bodies taken down before the Sabbath begins, but he needs to be certain they are dead. He sends soldiers to break their legs to hasten the deaths, but

> *when they came to Jesus and saw that he was already dead they did not break his legs. Instead, one of the soldiers pierced his side with a spear, and at once blood and water came out.* (John 19:33-34)

This provides absolute certainty that Jesus has died.

Present in his last hours, accompanying Jesus to his painful end, were his mother and closest friends: "*Near the cross of Jesus stood his mother and his mother's sister, Mary the wife of Clopas, and Mary Magdalene … and the disciple whom he loved*" (John 19:25-26). His loved ones could not directly assist Jesus in his agony, but they brought the precious gift of their presence to his dying.

In contrast to the stark description of the moment of Jesus' death, the gospels are very graphic in describing the response to Jesus' death: a great darkness descends; Mark describes the veil of the sanctuary being torn in two; Matthew describes an earthquake. All these represent an overwhelming cosmic sadness at the death of this innocent man who came to show us how much God loves us. In the Old Testament, death is personified as the enemy. It is associated with descent into the ultimate darkness where there is no joy, no hope, and total isolation. Jesus' raising of Lazarus symbolized his release from the power of death, but here on Calvary, Jesus freely lays down his life for us and our salvation. Jesus trusts in the Father's love and care even as he breathes his last. His trust is rewarded in the amazing resurrection, and we are brought salvation and eternal life as a consequence (Rolheiser, 2015).

DEATH COMES AS A STRANGER

In Jesus' time, death was a familiar event because it occurred in homes and communities. However, Jesus' death was exceptional in that it occurred in a public space of disgrace and as a direct result of intended violence, making it difficult for his loved ones to give him the usual care and comfort of the time.

Today we have little experience of the moment of death because it is hidden away in hospitals and long-term care facilities (Dugdale, 2015). We experience death as a medical diagnosis in sterile and unfamiliar contexts dominated by belief in medical technology's ability to avoid death indefinitely. Some use technology to freeze their bodies, waiting for a future cure.

Even the diagnosis of death has become complicated today. The universal human experience that you stopped breathing and you died or your heart stopped and you died is no longer a certainty. Since the 1950s, death has been progressively redefined from cessation of heart and lung function to brain death (President's Council on Bioethics, 2008). The notion of brain death entered medicine to permit the discontinuation of the newly developed mechanical ventilators when it was clear that the patient would not recover even though the lungs and heart could be kept going. Today, brain death is a central issue in organ donation when hearts and lungs are still functioning but brain function has been irreparably damaged. This change in the definition of the profound and permanent concept of death did not arise from deep theological or philosophical consideration, but from practical issues presented by technology.

Patients and their families in palliative care can experience a quiet and peaceful death at home surrounded by loved ones, but this is not the common experience. Death, that feared thing, comes to us all in unexpected trauma on the side of the road, in intensive care units and long-term care facilities, and in our homes. We fear this unfathomable and shared human experience of death, but it is real and inevitable. It cannot be avoided, no matter how sophisticated our technology. This inevitability may explain our cultural obsession with death:

in the fascination in movies and on television with forensic anthropologists, zombies and the undead. The inevitability, unpredictability and inherent mystery of death are reasons for the medically assisted death movement, where the only death considered "good" is a death we control on our own time and our own terms.

ROSA'S STORY OF A DIFFICULT DYING

Rosa is a 59-year-old happily married wife, mother and grandmother who was diagnosed with inflammatory breast cancer two years ago. Despite aggressive treatment, she has never gone into remission. The cancer spread widely and rapidly, so she has been in constant pain and distress. Rosa knows she is dying. After her second hospital admission for acute pain management six months ago, she and her husband, Miguel, chose home palliative care. She has lived longer than the medical team originally expected.

She is blessed by care from an excellent palliative care team that carefully attends to her physical, emotional and spiritual needs. She and Miguel are active members of their parish. Her pastor and members of the parish's pastoral care team are supportive of her and of Miguel. She wants to stay at home, but Miguel is in anguish as he sees her declining and convinces her she needs more help. She is admitted again to the hospital palliative care unit because of her unrelieved pain. She receives intravenous morphine, but despite aggressive treatment her pain is excruciating.

It is now day three, and Rosa is becoming increasingly drowsy. She tells Miguel that she has a powerful sense that she is dying and is ready for God to take her. As she and Miguel tearfully embrace, saying goodbye to each other, Rosa develops spasms that wrack her whole body every five to 10 seconds. The team increases her medications, but her pain and these spasms are out of control. Rosa is conscious and in severe distress, saying, "I am ready to die, but this is a nightmare." Miguel is finding it difficult to stay by her side when these wrenching movements occur. Her daughters cannot tolerate being in the room and are unable to bring the beloved grandchildren to say their goodbyes.

The skilled team is doing everything that usually relieves distressing symptoms like these. They could not achieve pain relief or control her spasms while Rosa, who is now having some breathing difficulty, and is actively dying, remains conscious. Rosa and Miguel were faithful Catholics who would never consider assisted death. After carefully reviewing options, and much prayer, the recommendation is to initiate continuous palliative sedation, in addition to her medications for pain control. Rosa is given continuous infusion of a combination of drugs to sedate her and becomes quiet and peaceful as she loses consciousness.

AT THE HOUR OF OUR DEATH

For patients, their loved ones and their caregivers, the moment of death is both a biological event and a sacred mystery. It is the finality of our life on earth. It can be terrifying for some and a moment of overwhelming peace for others, even in the midst of their sadness and loss.

In stark contrast to Jesus' time, the geography of death has moved from home and community to hospital, often in intensive care units, or long-term care facilities. Today we have little direct experience of death, hidden away as it is behind the walls of these institutions. It is not surprising that we don't know

REDISCOVERING THE ART OF DYING

what to expect as death approaches and when death occurs. Not only is the place of our death today different from the way it was before, but the trajectories or courses of our dying have changed as well (Lynn, 2005). Throughout history, death came rapidly after injury and infection to almost all. Jesus' death occurred after a short period because of its traumatic nature. Today, sudden death comes to many in accidents, cardiac arrest and stroke. In these tragic situations, there is no preparation for the death itself, and clinical and pastoral care focuses on the grieving loved ones.

But most patients today come to the moment of their death after long periods of illness along three well-recognized paths of dying: cancer; chronic illness and organ failure; and frailty and cognitive decline. In the cancer pathway that Rosa is on, patients either respond to initial treatment or do not respond and embark on a predictable decline to death. In the chronic illness and organ failure pathway, as experienced in heart failure and chronic respiratory disease seen in Shirley's story in Chapter 1 and Colleen's story in Chapter 2, patients have a long and complicated course. These patients experience a turbulent course with periods of good function and quality of life interspersed with health crises. The path of dying is downward, but with multiple medical rescues along the way. Some of these patients have been to the brink of death and back many times, making it difficult when the hour of death finally arrives. In the frailty pathway dramatically demonstrated in Gladys' story in Chapter 5, there is a slow but steady degradation of health and cognitive function. While the path of death differs, the final hour of our anticipated deaths is similar.

Rosa, Miguel and their family need to be prepared for the moment of death even as we recognize that no preparation can anticipate all outcomes. Patients and families do ask, "When?" "What will it be like?" It is often noted ironically that in medicine, the only instrument with 100 percent accuracy is the retrospect-o-scope! Of course there is no such instrument. More to the point, there is no medical instrument that can accurately predict the exact hour of death. But we do have signs it is getting close. Prognostication is difficult not just because of a lack of current knowledge, but also because of the inherent fallibility in medicine (Downing, 2011).

THE LAST HOURS OF LIVING

Rosa and her loved ones can be helped by knowledge of what the last hours might look like and how death will come (Ferris et al., 2011). The usual road to death involves an increasing drowsiness and difficulty in communicating, which can be very frustrating for loved ones. There can be loss of ability to swallow and distressing loss of bowel and bladder control. Changes in breathing are marked. There can be long periods in which the dying patient is quiet and still except for noisy breathing caused by secretions, the ominously named "death rattle." Then, the patient slips into coma and has a quiet death.

Unfortunately, Rosa is travelling a difficult road to death, which is quite different. It can involve hyperactive delirium (an irreversible state of confusion associated with significant patient distress, restlessness, muscle spasms, agitation and hallucinations). There can be moaning, which is often mistaken for pain and can be difficult to distinguish from death anxiety and spiritual crisis. Death anxiety is a complex blend of thoughts and emotions including a dread of death, essential feelings of loneliness, and extreme anger and despair at having no control (Firestone & Catlett, 2009). This is not the ordinary sadness and anger of the dying, but an overwhelming darkness of spirit sometimes referred to as terminal angst.

Rosa is experiencing the distressing symptom of myoclonus – muscle spasms with violent jerks and restless, purposeless movements, often seen with difficult dying. It is a frightening and distressing symptom for both the conscious patient and their loved ones. Rosa is now actively dying, but her last hours have become a nightmare for her and her family. She cannot pray and she cannot have the comfort of her loved ones at her bedside. Physicians, nurses, ethicists and pastoral care providers would all recognize Rosa's as a "hard case," which can bring distress to all involved.

CARE AT THE END OF LIFE

In Chapter 6, we identified the factors that patients and families consider important in end-of-life care, including effective pain and symptom control, trust in the health care team, avoidance of unwanted technology, effective communication, continuity of care, and the opportunity for life's completion compatible with life values. These factors resonate with the long-standing Christian understanding of a *good death*. Palliative care aims to balance provision of effective medical care for pain and other symptoms with attention to these psychosocial and spiritual challenges at end of life. It also directly addresses care of the dying person and for their loved ones. Even with the assistance of excellent palliative care, Rosa's medical situation is making it difficult for her to have a peaceful death and for her loved ones to comfort and support her.

Dying patients, like Rosa, commonly receive sedatives for pain control. Symptom relief is generally achieved while maintaining consciousness. Maintaining the balance between comfort and the awareness needed to attend to spiritual issues is now a serious matter for Rosa and all involved in her care and accompaniment.

As devout Catholics, Rosa and Miguel are comforted to know that Church teaching recognizes that appropriate pain management can serve as

> organic and psychic relief making prayer easier and enabling one to give oneself more generously ... help

to make the course of the illness less dramatic and contribute to the humanization and acceptance of death. (Pontifical Council for Pastoral Assistance to Health Care Workers, 1995)

However, when pain and symptom distress become intolerable and interfere with communication among loved ones and with completion of the spiritual tasks of dying, the issue of continuous palliative sedation arises. Palliative sedation is the lowering of patient consciousness using medication for the purpose of limiting awareness of suffering that is intractable and intolerable. Palliative care physicians will consider it when alternatives are ineffective for an imminently dying patient with the intention of relieving symptoms, not ending life (Kirk et al., 2010).

Because the Catholic understanding is that death is not just a passive event but an active and free final confirmation of life and faith, every minute in the hour of our death counts. Maintaining consciousness to deal with the relational and spiritual last things and to appreciate the care received is crucial and must not be suppressed without a serious reason (International Association of Catholic Bioethicists, 2012). This notion of justification for a serious reason is not new:

> painkillers that cause unconsciousness need special consideration. For a person not only has to be able to satisfy his or her moral duties and family obligations; he or she also has to prepare himself or herself with full consciousness for meeting Christ. Thus Pius XII warns: "It is not right to deprive the dying person of consciousness without a serious reason." (Sacred Congregation for the Doctrine of the Faith, 1980, 514)

Because of this spiritual significance of dying, Catholic reflections on palliative sedation have identified concerns with the concept and its use (Belgrave & Requena, 2012). Issues requiring prayer and pastoral discernment include the need for assurance that palliative sedation does not hasten death, distinguishing palliative sedation from assisted death and the spiritual and moral significance of consciousness in preparing for death (O'Rourke, 1992). These issues need to be addressed with Rosa, her family and her caregivers.

Carefully titrated palliative sedation does not hasten death. Even if the evidence is not completely accurate and there is some risk, the Church teaches that

> The use of painkillers to alleviate the sufferings of the dying, even at the risk of shortening their days, can be morally in conformity with human dignity if death is not willed as either an end or a means, but only foreseen and tolerated as inevitable. (*Catechism of the Catholic Church*, no. 2279)

The initiation of palliative sedation is intended to re-lieve unbearable and intractable suffering in the imminently dying when nothing else has helped to maintain the balance between symptom control and facilitating the completion of life's spiritual, psychological and relational tasks. Intention is key, but it is not the only criterion. Traditional Catholic moral theology developed the principle of double effect to recognize that our actions have both intended and unintended effects. Good intent is crucial. But the action in itself must be good: the unintended effect must not be the means to accomplish the primary benefit and there must be proportionality between the intended and unintended effects (Boyle, 2004). This principle is very helpful in understanding the issue as an example of intending pain relief in an intolerable situation and accepting loss of awareness.

A *good death* can be a peaceful and quiet time of transition but, as Jesus' death graphically demonstrates, it can also be complex and painful. Rosa has prayerfully prepared for her dying, but her situation is compromising her final hours. Rosa's daughters bring the grandchildren in to kiss their *abuela* good-bye. She appears to them to be sleeping, and the five-year-old muses, "I think Abuela needs a good sleep because it's a very long trip to heaven." Eight hours later, Rosa dies peacefully with Miguel and her daughters at her side.

QUESTIONS FOR REFLECTION

- Have you been present at the moment of, or leading up to, someone's death?

- What was that like for you?

- How do you feel about, imagine or think of your own inevitable death?

- Are you okay with the unknowable, mysterious quality of our own mortality and inevitable death?

- Have you experienced the loss of more than one loved one?

- How were/are those losses different?

9

Rituals and the Ministry of Consolation: Jesus Is Buried

When evening had come, and since it was the day of Preparation, that is, the day before the sabbath, Joseph of Arimathea, a respected member of the council, who was also himself waiting expectantly for the kingdom of God, went boldly to Pilate and asked for the body of Jesus. Then Pilate wondered if he were already dead; and summoning the centurion, he asked him whether he had been dead for some time. When he learned from the centurion that he was dead, he granted the body to Joseph. Then Joseph bought a linen cloth, and taking down the body, wrapped it in the linen cloth, and laid it in a tomb that had been hewn out of the rock. He then rolled a stone against the door of the tomb. Mary Magdalene and Mary the mother of Joses saw where the body was laid. (Mark 15:42-47)

The grieving Mary, John and the others who stood at the foot of the cross during Jesus' dying and death have left the scene. We can only imagine the profound and paralyzing sense of loss they are experiencing.

The proper burial of Jesus is important to those who loved him, as their last act of care and respect. Scriptures reveal a puzzling absence of the apostles at the moment of Jesus' death and burial, so the request for the body of Jesus was made by a newcomer to the Passion story, Joseph of Arimathea, who *"went boldly to Pilate and asked for the body of Jesus."* Boldness was required because the Romans forbade burial of the crucified to reinforce their status as outcasts and to cruelly punish their families. So, Joseph boldly goes where none of the apostles dared to go.

We are told that Joseph was an observant Jew *"who was also himself waiting expectantly for the kingdom of God"* (Mark 15:43). Luke tells us, *"Now there was a good and righteous man named Joseph, who, though a member of the council, had not agreed to their plan and action"* (Luke 23:50-51). John reveals that Joseph *"was a disciple of Jesus, though a secret one because of his fear of the Jews"* (John 19:38). Joseph was a wealthy and distinguished member of the council of the Sanhedrin, a devout Jew who knew the importance of rituals regarding burying the dead, even criminals. He comes prepared with a new linen shroud in which to receive the body of Christ from the cross.

Joseph is assisted in Jesus' burial by another newcomer to the story, for we are told that *"Nicodemus, who had at first come to Jesus by night, also came, bringing a mixture of myrrh and aloes, weighing about a hundred pounds"* (John 19:39). Nicodemus, a secret follower, who came to Jesus at night, now helps to bury him at night. The burial was done quickly because the Sabbath was about to begin. The body was placed in a tomb and anointed with spices, according to Jewish tradition.

The scriptures are clear and consistent that Jesus was given a very specific burial site, which was noted by Mary of Magdala and Mary the mother of Joses, so it could be found again (Brown, 1994). And, despite considerable danger to themselves, the women return to the grave to complete the burial rituals: "*When the Sabbath was over, Mary Magdalene, and Mary the mother of James, and Salome bought spices, so that they might go and anoint him*" (Mark 16:1).

Even as some of Jesus' closest disciples seem so overcome by grief or fear that they do not participate, the rituals of Jewish burial are important to other followers to show their love and final respect for Jesus. The rituals carry them forward in the paralysis of their grief and overwhelming loss. Religious burial rituals are still important for believers today. But the social context of funerals and burials is undergoing significant transformation, challenging these as celebrations of a resurrection people.

MICHAEL'S STORY OF A GOOD LIFE AND A *GOOD DEATH*

Suddenly and much too soon, at 70 years of age, Michael died. The well-loved husband of Ann, his devoted wife of almost 50 years, and the father of their children, Beth and Dan, Michael was gone with little notice or preparation, leaving a desolated family.

Michael was an outgoing, take-charge fellow. His dedication to work was surpassed only by his love and faithful presence to family, church and community. He had never been ill so, typically, on the night he had some chest pain, he drove himself to the hospital. He did not want to disturb anyone else and assumed that it was a minor problem.

On his arrival at the hospital, it was clear this was far from minor; Michael was having a major heart attack. He was admitted to the intensive care unit and his family was urgently summoned. The stunned family members gathered hastily to confront the unbelievable reality that Michael was dying. They had no warning and no preparation for this. Their world was shattered. Through their shock and grief, Ann knew they needed to call for a priest to give Michael his final anointing and to pray with them.

During life he often said, "We die the way we live," and that was true for Michael. Over the relatively short 62 hours from his admission to hospital to his death, he was prayerfully surrounded by family and a multitude of friends who came to say goodbye and to support the family. Michael died a *good death*, hearing his favourite prayer, the rosary, being recited by the surrounding family and friends.

The family was paralyzed by the suddenness of his death and almost incapable of making practical decisions. They were carried through the days immediately following Michael's death by the familiar Catholic rituals of a wake and a funeral Mass. During the wake, the community fire department held an around-the-clock vigil for their beloved Honorary Fire Chief. The funeral Mass had an overflow crowd, with many relatives and friends spilling over into the church auditorium. The colourful 4th Degree Knights of Columbus and members of the fire department made an honour guard that Michael would have loved.

Family members wept for a loved one taken much too soon from this life. They were sustained in these early days of loss by the presence and support of relatives and friends, and carried by the rhythm and flow of familiar faith-filled rituals.

In the Catholic tradition, visiting the sick and burying the dead are corporal works of mercy. Consoling the afflicted and praying for the living and the dead are spiritual works of mercy. All of these acts are essential elements in care for the sick, dying and bereaved today.

FUNERALS AND BURIAL RITUALS

By the tender mercy of our God, the dawn from on high will break upon us, to give light to those who sit in darkness and in the shadow of death, to guide our feet into the way of peace. (Luke 1:78-79)

All faiths and cultures have rituals for care of the dead and bereaved. These rituals are activities involving actions, words and objects performed in a prescribed manner that have a sacred symbolism (Lazenby et al., 2014). Throughout the ages, burial rituals have been provided by diverse communities that have understood the funeral as the final rite of passage. These rituals relieve the grieving of decision making during the confused and vulnerable time of living through "the shadow of death."

There has been a departure from religious rituals of passage in all aspects of Western society, including coming to adulthood and marriage. Many avoid traditional religious rituals of death and burial for a variety of reasons, including the need to get it "over with" and move on (Cann, 2014). But there is still a deep human need for ritual, as vividly demonstrated in the influence of professional sports, the religion of our time.

Rituals play an important role in meaning making in grief and loss. So, it is not surprising that new, highly personal "celebrations of life" are constantly being created. Generally, these celebrate the superficial aspects of an individual's life, such as being a rabid sports fan or a model train collector. Reflective of secular and individualistic societies, these celebrations lack a shared, communal dimension to loss and a sense of death's transcendent meaning.

Funerals perform important practical functions, including removal of the body, a final rite and burial. They benefit the mourners by confirming the reality of the death, providing help with the expression of loss, stimulating positive memories of the deceased, and identifying the need of the bereaved to move on with changed relationships after the burial. Funerals acknowledge that death is both an individual and a communal experience. They provide a context of shared meaning and community values that bind the mourners together and help to diminish some of the isolation and loneliness of grief (Rando, 1984).

Michael's Catholic funeral reflected the community's identity as a resurrection people. The Easter candle was lit at his funeral because even in the painful experience of his death, the community witnesses to faith and hope in the resurrection. Michael's life was celebrated in light of the fact that he was baptized and redeemed through Christ's death and resurrection. The funeral prayers and liturgical actions manifested the dignity, unity and sacredness of Michael's life, and his remains recall his life as a baptized child of God.

Comfort and support for Michael's mourning family and friends was central to the funeral liturgy. They were prayed for at the beginning and end of the funeral. The funeral also renewed the mourners' faith in the resurrection and life eternal:

In him the hope of blessed resurrection has dawned, that those saddened by the certainty of dying, might be consoled by the promise of immortality to come. Indeed for your faithful, Lord, life is changed not ended, and, when this earthly dwelling turns to dust, an eternal dwelling is made ready for them in heaven. (Preface I for the Dead, International Committee on English in the Liturgy, 1990)

Prayers for Michael himself were said throughout the liturgy, reassuring all that he was gone but still connected to his loved ones and his God. Michael's death and burial, marked by farewells from family and community and the Catholic rituals he knew and loved well, was a fitting completion of his life story. Because of his deep involvement with the Church, a funeral Mass, rather than a simple funeral liturgy, was celebrated for Michael.

The final prayers asked for the comfort of God, the Father of mercies, to comfort the grieving. The funeral ends with a challenge to the entire community to support one another in the painful time to come.

MOURNING FOR JESUS

He then rolled a stone against the door of the tomb. (Mark 15:46)

The burial of Jesus marked the end of his earthly life, but it was only the beginning of the grief and mourning of his loved ones. Some images can help us ponder the different ways in which they were grieving.

Scripture does not find words for the grief of Mary, the "Mother of Sorrows." But, Michelangelo's *Pietà,* which is worth far more than a thousand words, captures the grieving mother receiving the bruised and battered body of her beloved son on her lap. The masterpiece calls forth a poignant image of the many times Mary held the baby Jesus on her lap. We can only imagine how this holy and faithful mother feels the loss.

Chosen to lead the community of disciples after Jesus' death, the impetuous Peter's denial was foretold by Jesus. Despite his protestations of fidelity, Peter denies Jesus repeatedly. When, in the courtyard, he is reminded of Jesus' prophecy, "*he went out and wept bitterly*" (Matthew 26:69-75). Rolheiser suggests that Peter's denial of Jesus not only moves him out of the courtyard but outside of the circle of discipleship (Rolheiser, 2015). Imagine how Peter's grief at the loss of Jesus is compounded by his knowledge of his own weakness and infidelity at the end.

Judas' betrayal makes his grief even more deep and dark:

When Judas, his betrayer, saw that Jesus was condemned, he repented and brought back the thirty pieces of silver to the chief priests and the elders. He said, "I have sinned by betraying innocent blood."… Throwing down the pieces of silver in the temple, he departed; and he went and hanged himself. (Matthew 27:3-5)

Judas' grief was so marked by guilt that he could find no way to live with his weakness.

Mary Magdalene, one of Jesus' intimate friends, came early to complete the burial rites. She "*stood weeping outside the tomb*" (John 20:11). Mary's whole world was shattered as she witnessed his death and burial. She lost her beloved Jesus and her entire world of belief. She grieved openly but still found the strength to complete his burial rites.

Peter, James and John, the apostles closest to Jesus, slept in the garden of Gethsemane because of their "*grief*" (Luke 22:45). This was grief at the loss of their expected vision of the reign of God, and an anticipatory grief for what was to come. All of the apostles except Judas fled and hid in the upper room: "*the doors of the house where the disciples had met were locked for fear of the Jews*" (John 20:19).

The disciples on the road to Emmaus are described as "*looking sad.*" "*But we had hoped that he was the one to redeem Israel*" (Luke 24:17-21). They don't recognize Jesus because they feel overwhelmed by loss and are without hope. Jesus did not live up to their expectations, and their faith and trust were betrayed. In their grief, they are despondent, desperately trying to understand the meaning of all that has happened.

The loss of a loved one brings profound challenges of meaning and hope to all. Mourning can be a time of great grace or a time of loss of faith.

MICHAEL'S LOSS AND WRITING A NEW FAMILY STORY

Walking away from the grave, this was a moment of family grief never to be forgotten. Ann was being held up by Beth, who was trying to be strong for her mother. Beth glanced back to see the attendants closing the grave. In the overwhelming horror of that reality, she silently screamed, "No, no, please don't do that to my precious dad!" Dan, who had been estranged from his father, walked alone to his car.

Sustained by the funeral rituals immediately after Michael's sudden death, each member of his family is now mourning in their own way. Ann, who had been totally dependent on her beloved Michael, is feeling utterly lost. Her identity as wife and mother is changed radically. She is no longer part of a couple and the dream of future golden years together is gone. Beth, who is very much like her father, is trying to keep things together for her mother. Inside her is a deep sadness she dares not address in case she falls apart. Dan, whose relationship with his father had been stormy, gives brief hugs to his mother and sister. Then, in silence, he heads back to his home 200 miles away.

THE UNIQUENESS OF OUR GRIEF AND MOURNING

Friends and the local community provided wonderful support for Ann and her children at the time of Michael's death and burial. Their attention will now shift as life, for them, goes on unchanged. But long after the casserole dishes have been returned, and the thank you notes for sympathy cards mailed,

Michael's loved ones will be mourning, because their individual lives and life as a family have been changed forever.

Grief is a unique personal experience of loss. It has physical, psychological, social and spiritual dimensions (Kelley, 2010). Bereavement is the state of loss. Mourning is the process of dealing with the loss. Grief can bring a paralyzing numbness from the sheer intensity of the dying, whether it was sudden, as with Michael, or over a long and difficult period of time. There can be relief that the ordeal is over, even in sadness. Many feel consolation in knowing that their loved one is now at peace with God and all their pain and suffering is over.

The bereaved can feel an overwhelming sense of loss, disorientation and isolation. Sadness, loneliness, anger and guilt can be suddenly and torrentially triggered by words, actions, events such as birthdays and Christmas, and by nothing at all. Bereavement can affect health with an increased risk of depression, anxiety and general health complaints. There is a risk of mortality and suicide.

Each member of Michael's family is mourning in different ways. It is important to understand that these differences can be a source of ongoing suffering for families and friends. The most common pathway of mourning includes sadness and a low-grade depression, but little regret regarding the death because of a happy relationship with the deceased and an acceptance of death. Other pathways include a deep sadness but one filled with great comfort from fond memories of the deceased, the development of chronic depression, a chronic grief after a long, difficult experience of dying and death, and even the relief of depression present before death because it ends a chronic stressor.

Grief research has now rejected the "stages" understanding of dying and grief as too prescriptive of the "right way" to die (Kübler-Ross, 1969). We know that there is no right or wrong way to mourn, and no schedule for mourning that forces the bereaved to "get over it" and "move on" before they are ready. Central in grief and mourning are the affirmation of loss, the reconstruction of meaning, and finding ways to continue the bonds with the deceased (Neimeyer, 2000). Each of them will need to find ways to continue their bond with Michael as he lives on in memory and in their legacy. Some bereaved have a powerful sense of the presence of a loved one who has died, but others do not.

Michael's death presents a crisis of meaning to his loved ones regarding their understanding of the world, their own identity and their relationship to God. Each member of Michael's family now needs to create a new life story for themselves and for the family. In this task, they need the help of the community.

THE MINISTRY OF CONSOLATION

> The responsibility for the ministry of consolation rests with the believing community, which heeds the words and example of the Lord Jesus: "Blessed are they who mourn; they shall be consoled" (Matthew 5:3). (Liturgy Office of the Bishops' Conference of England and Wales and International Commission of Catholic Bishops' Conferences, 2005)

Ann can express her deep sadness at the loss of her beloved husband. There are days she finds her grief unbearable. She finds comfort in wonderful memories of the positive and faithful relationship they had over the years, and in her faith. But she has to cope with the loneliness of being a widow, in everything from sleeping alone for the first time in 50 years to recognizing her high dependence on Michael for all practical decisions about finances and home maintenance. Her identity as a wife and as part of a social couple is challenged. She doesn't know where she fits anymore.

Beth is trying to suppress her sadness and sense of abandonment to be strong for her mother. She, too, has very positive memories of her father. She is comforted by the fact that her father loved her, and that he knew she loved him. She believes her father would want her to support her mother. She keeps busy taking care of all the practical demands after a death, from cleaning out her father's closet to issues of banking and house upkeep. She tries to reach out to her brother but really does not understand his stoic, silent response to the death.

Dan is at great risk in his loss. He is filled with regret and guilt that he and his father were not close. He has not been a churchgoer since he left home, but he did find the rituals comforting. He finds some solace in the fact that he made it to his father's deathbed. He has always had difficulty expressing his emotions and was not able to say anything to his dying father. He did hold his dad's hand, and prayed for the first time in years. He doesn't know what his father's death means for him and his relationship with his family, and he doesn't know where to get help. He will need support from his family and may need professional assistance with grief work.

But we do not want you to be uninformed, brothers and sisters, about those who have died, so that you may not grieve as others do who have no hope. (1 Thessalonians 4:13)

Even though there may be dark days when it feels as if belief has fled, Michael's family can now be consoled by belief in God's faithfulness and a radical trust that the God who brought us to life will see us through death. As a resurrection people, we know that love endures as we move into an unimaginable and joyful future. Belief in the communion of the saints affirms our continuing bonds with those who have died.

These consoling beliefs are important. The experience of the ministry of care and consolation provided within the faith community provides those who mourn with active, tangible evidence of the ever-present, unending love of God. As medically assisted death becomes more common, it will present serious pastoral challenges to our understanding of care and consolation.

QUESTIONS FOR REFLECTION

- How do you respond to the grief of Jesus' loved ones?

- Which elements in the story of Michael's family are important to you?

- What is your most powerful personal experience of loss of a loved one? What role did rituals play for you?

- How might you help console and support the bereaved in your family?

- Loss can create opportunities for new personal and family stories, but unresolved grief can cause lifelong suffering. How can the faith community assist each of these?

IO

Do Not Be Afraid: Jesus Rises from the Dead

But on the first day of the week, at early dawn, they came to the tomb, taking the spices that they had prepared. They found the stone rolled away from the tomb, but when they went in, they did not find the body. While they were perplexed about this, suddenly two men in dazzling clothes stood beside them. The women were terrified and bowed their faces to the ground, but the men said to them, "Why do you look for the living among the dead? He is not here, but has risen." (Luke 24:1-6)

When we rolled the stone and left Jesus in the tomb, his life story appeared to be a great tragedy. The glorious promise of the reign of God appears to be unfulfilled (Navone, 1984). But God writes the surprise ending to end all surprise endings for the story of Jesus, the Christ. The cross was the climax of the story in its test of Jesus' fidelity to his mission, but the final resolution of the story of Jesus comes with that same stone rolled away on Easter. With the discovery of the empty tomb by faithful women and the astonishing, life- and cosmic-transforming message from men in brilliant clothing, everything is changed. The tragedy is transformed into a heroic epic of love and courage with deep meaning for all who tell it.

The women are, understandably, terrified when they see the empty tomb and receive the shining messengers. This "terrified" is the same word, *ekthambeisthai*, meaning "shaken to the core," that Mark used for Jesus' prayer in Gethsemane (Martin, 2014). The women run to tell the eleven of these amazing events.

For centuries, the celebration of the Stations of the Cross ended with the darkness of the burial of Jesus. But this is not the full story. The darkness and sadness of the Way of the Cross finds light and inestimable joy in the way of the resurrection (Byer, 2013). Reflections on the words and actions of Jesus after the resurrection give us insights into how to be a resurrection people. Three themes are clear: Jesus' constant assurance that we need not be afraid; the inability of even his closest friends to recognize him until he first reaches out in a personal sign of loving intimacy and then reveals the full meaning of the scriptures in the breaking of the bread; and a final commissioning of the disciples and of all believers to live as witnesses to the resurrection.

Jesus' constant greeting to the disciple was *"Do not be afraid"* (Matthew 28:10). He needed to reassure them that his shocking reappearance, which is beyond human understanding, is a manifestation of the love and care of God. The same message of "be not afraid," in the presence of the inexplicable, was given to Mary and Joseph at the Incarnation. Nothing is impossible for God.

> *The death he died, he died to sin, once for all; but the life he lives, he lives to God.* (Romans 6:10)

The resurrection will convince the disciples that death has not triumphed or ended a real and living relationship with the Lord. But each of the disciples fails to recognize Jesus when he first appears to them. Of course they do. They have just lost Jesus to death. They have no expectations of ever seeing him again.

Each needs some intimate, personal sign from Jesus before they can see him. Mary Magdalene recognizes Jesus when he says her name. The disciples, including Peter, were fishing unsuccessfully when Jesus appears and calls out from the shore about their catch. Although they do not recognize him, they cast their net on the other side of the boat at his suggestion. When it overflows with fish, the impetuous Peter knows immediately that it is the Lord and jumps into the water to meet him. On their reunion, Jesus gives Peter three chances to make amends for his threefold denial, and a great responsibility to care for his flock.

The eleven are huddled together in fear when Jesus appears to them and says, "*Peace be with you*" (Luke 24:36). The apostles think they are seeing a ghost. Jesus asks them to touch him to verify that he is real, and eats with them to prove he is alive, before he opens the scriptures to them and gives them his peace and power to forgive sins. The doubtful Thomas, who was not present when Jesus appeared to the other apostles, makes a rather outrageous demand for proof of real physical contact. He does not trust the experience of the other disciples and says, "*Unless I see the mark of the nails in his hands, and put my finger in the mark of the nails and my hand in his side, I will not believe*" (John 20:25). Jesus returns and gives Thomas an opportunity to do just that.

Disciples on the road to Emmaus are so downcast that they barely even glance at the stranger who walks with them. Jesus puts the events of the Passion in the context of scripture and the history of salvation, and they finally recognize him in the breaking of the bread.

Finally, all the disciples are commissioned to proclaim the good news before Jesus leaves them in the Ascension. On

Pentecost, the Holy Spirit descends to be with them and us in the journey.

History can verify that Jesus died, and it cannot refute the resurrection (Licona, 2010). Only faith can recognize and accept it. We live in the hope of the resurrection, for nothing is impossible with God, and this is a source of overwhelming joy. Resurrection is the light after the darkness of the Passion and death. Jesus came to conquer sin, suffering and death. We still get sick and suffer and die, but Jesus has conquered them all. And he inspires and strengthens us to work to overcome the evils that foster suffering and death. Death is not the end for Christians. It is a transition to a new and everlasting life in the heart of God. From Incarnation, through suffering and death, to resurrection, God's love is more powerful than sin and death.

Swimming against the tide: prophetic resistance

The medieval art of dying was firmly rooted in shared belief in the life, death and resurrection of Jesus Christ and in care for the sick and dying provided by families and communities. Neither of these supports is present today.

We live in a post-Christian and post-Christendom society. Laws and rules are no longer supportive of Christian spiritual and moral beliefs. The communal sense of mutuality and responsibility for the care and protection of its members no longer dominates our increasingly professionalized socio-cultural landscape (McKnight, 1995). We also live in a world where technology is used in the hope of relieving suffering and finding happiness in all aspects of life. In health care, drugs and devices are used to reshape faces and bodies in sometimes addictive attempts to find beauty, to relieve all emotional and psychological distress in an "instant-relief" society, and even to try and find inner peace.

Swimming against the tide of medically assisted death is an urgent challenge today. While heralded by many as humane and compassionate care, assisted death – both assisted suicide and euthanasia – is, in essence, a rejection of the Paschal Mystery, the suffering, death and resurrection of Jesus Christ. Jesus accepted his suffering and lived through it to the end. He trusted in the Father's love and care for him, and his reward is beyond human imagination. It is resurrection and life eternal for him and all who believe in him.

Medically assisted death is the medicalization of human suffering and of death itself. We need to show prophetic resistance to this inappropriate use of technology. Suffering is a total human, emotional and spiritual experience. It requires attention to the deeper issues of meaning in life. Suffering is helped by presence and accompaniment in this search for meaning.

UNTOLD STORIES AND PROPHETIC WITNESS

Do you not know that all of us who have been baptized into Christ Jesus were baptized into his death? Therefore we have been buried with him by baptism into death, so that, just as Christ was raised from the dead by the glory of the Father, so we too might walk in newness of life. For if we have been united with him in a death like his, we will certainly be united with him in a resurrection like his. (Romans 6:3-6)

In these reflections, our stories have told of confident, competent individuals with clear plans for their futures becoming totally captured by issues of serious illness, and faced with complex and risky medical choices. We have seen the natural human tendency to avoid the reality of serious medical issues. We have seen some patients' pathological denial of the limits of medicine caught in an endless pursuit of a cure, which prevents their acceptance of dying and damages family relationships. We have heard stories that vividly depicted young lives changed forever by chronic and debilitating illness and overwhelmed by what their future holds. Poignant stories of the lives of elders experiencing isolation, loneliness and loss of independence tell of our human interdependence. We have identified central issues of the loss of dignity, the loss of identity and meaning making in physical illness and in cognitive decline, and the significance of our responses. We have seen peaceful death and difficult dying, and the need for support in preparing for dying today. Our stories show sickness, dying and bereavement as times of great grace for some, and of devastating pain and spiritual crisis for others.

These stories are based on real health care encounters today. The environment of health care is dominated by a technical fix and cure approach, while modern bioethics focuses on patient autonomy narrowly understood as rational choice. We know that respect for persons is about more than their decisional competence. It requires a reverence for life stories. Our reflections have shown the importance of our spiritual and moral beliefs in our practical health care decisions and choices.

RESURRECTION HOPE AND THE EVANGELIZING COMMUNITY

Then Jesus went about all the cities and villages, teaching in their synagogues, proclaiming the good news of the kingdom, and curing every disease and every sickness. (Matthew 9:35)

The resurrection challenges and empowers us to become an evangelizing community of disciples of Jesus Christ, witnessing in a transformative way to his healing and reconciling ministry today. It moves us from words to action in developing environments of support and care that provide tangible experiences of God's mercy and lessen the suffering of the sick, chronically ill, frail and dependent elderly, the dying and the bereaved. The resurrection impels us into the civic space to advocate for just health care and for protection of the most vulnerable among us. The resurrection demands that we accept the commission of being an evangelizing community.

> An evangelizing community ... has an endless desire to show mercy, the fruit of its own experience of the power of the Father's infinite mercy ... An evangelizing community gets involved by word and deed in people's lives; it bridges distances, it is willing to abase itself if necessary and it embraces human life, touching the suffering flesh of Christ in others. An evangelizing community is also supportive, standing by people at every step of the way, no matter how difficult or lengthy this may prove to be. (Pope Francis, *Evangelii Gaudium,* 2013, no. 24)

Transforming into a resurrection people is hard. Jesus paid the price for resurrection through his suffering and death. Can we pay the cost of discipleship? Assisted death has provided a new urgency for us to touch "the suffering flesh in others." It compels us to move out of the comfortable pew, accept the cost of discipleship, and become actively engaged in the lives of people, especially the vulnerable and those on the peripheries.

"I was sick and you took care of me...." (Matthew 25:36)

With medical advances and systems with highly trained health professionals, we have all come to expect that all the needs of the sick and dying will be provided by public services. We have forgotten that as disciples of Christ, we are all called to proclaim the Good News, comfort the afflicted and care for the sick. Jesus' cures involved physical care, healing of the whole person – body, mind and spirit – and restoration of the sick to the community. These include the acutely ill, those suffering chronic physical and mental illness and disability, the dying and the bereaved.

An art of dying in the post-Christian world

If one member suffers, all suffer.... (1 Corinthians 12:26)

An art of dying for a resurrection people in our post-Christian, individualistic, technologically dominated world will require great faith and courage to swim against the tide of medically assisted death. It will require a commitment to prophetic resistance to the inappropriate use of technology, and prophetic witness to God's love and mercy, especially for those who suffer.

We need to be bold in identifying the real meaning of compassion:

> A society unable to accept its suffering members and incapable of helping share their suffering and to bear it inwardly through "com-passion" is a cruel and inhuman society ... Indeed, to accept the "other" who suffers means that I take up his suffering in such a way that it becomes mine also ... The Latin word *con-solatio*, consolation, expresses this beautifully. It suggests *being with* the other in his solitude, so that it ceases to be solitude. (Pope Benedict XVI, *Spe Salvi*, 2007, no. 38)

We need to accept that

> Mercy is concerned with more than justice; it is a matter of attentiveness and sensitivity to the concrete needs we encounter. It is a matter of overcoming the focus on ourselves that makes us deaf and blind to the physical and spiritual needs of others. (Kasper, 2013)

These understandings of compassion and mercy will demand much of us as we respond to the needs of the sick and suffering among us. None of it will be possible without our personal conversion to the mind and heart of Jesus. This conversion requires our personal acceptance of the Way of the Cross in our own lives. Crosses abound in our lives, and suffering is not optional. But Jesus has lived through suffering and death for us. He knows our suffering. He is the glorious and joyful sign of God's promise that in his dying, he has destroyed death.

> *"For God so loved the world that he gave his only Son, so that everyone who believes in him may not perish but may have eternal life."* (John 3:16)

QUESTIONS FOR REFLECTION

- How do you respond to the empty tomb?

- What do you think it means to be a resurrection people?

- What stories of sickness, suffering, dependence, dying and mourning came to your mind during these reflections?

- What is the story we will write that is worthy of the story of Jesus?

- How important are prophetic resistance and witness in our rejection of medically assisted death?

- What are the biggest obstacles to our transformation into an evangelizing community?

- How willing are you to suffer and to touch the suffering flesh in others?

BIBLIOGRAPHY

Albom, M. (2002). *Tuesdays with Morrie: An Old Man, A Young Man, and Life's Greatest Lesson*. New York: Broadway Books.

Ashley, B.M., & O'Rourke, K.D. (1997). *Health Care Ethics: A Theological Analysis* (4th ed.). Washington, DC: Georgetown University Press.

Baylis, F. (2017). Still Gloria: personal identity and dementia. *International Journal of Feminist Approaches to Bioethics*, 10(1), 210–224.

Beard, R.L. (2004). In their voices: identity preservation and experiences of Alzheimer's disease. *Journal of Aging Studies*, 18(4), 415–428.

Beauchamp, T. L., & Childress, J.F. (1994). *Principles of Biomedical Ethics* (4th ed.). New York: Oxford University Press.

Belgrave, K., & Requena, P. (2012). A primer on palliative sedation. *The National Catholic Bioethics Quarterly*, 12(2), 263–281.

Bernadin, J. (1997). *The Gift of Peace*. Chicago: Loyola Press.

Boyle, J. (2004). Medical ethics and double effect: the case of terminal sedation. *Theoretical Medicine and Bioethics*, 25(1), 51–60.

Breitbart, W., Rosenfeld, B., Pessin, H., Kaim, M., Funesti-Esch, J., Galietta, M., Nelson, C.J., & Brescia, R. (2000). Depression, hopelessness, and desire for hastened death in terminally ill patients with cancer. *JAMA,* 284(22), 2907–2911.

Brown, R.E. (1994). *The Death of the Messiah: From Gethsemane to the Grave: A Commentary on the Passion in the Four Gospels* (2 vols.). New York: Doubleday.

Brown Coughlan, P. (1993). *Facing Alzheimer's: Family Caregivers Speak.* New York: Ballantine Books.

Buckman, R. (1993). *How to Break Bad News: A Guide for Healthcare Professionals.* London: Macmillan.

Byer, G. (2013). *Via Lucis: The Way of Light.* Toronto: Novalis.

Byock, I. (2013). *The Best Care Possible.* New York: Avery.

Cann, C. (2014). *Virtual Afterlives: Grieving the Dead in the Twenty-First Century.* Lexington, KY: University of Kentucky Press.

Caprio, A.J. (2016). Palliative care: renaming as supportive care and integration into comprehensive care. *CMAJ,* 188(10), 711–712.

Cassell, E. (1991). *The Nature of Suffering and the Goals of Medicine.* New York: Oxford University Press.

Catechism of the Catholic Church. (1993). Vatican City: Libreria Editrice Vaticana. http://www.vatican.va/archive/ENG0015/_INDEX.HTM.Chochinov, H.M. (2012). *Dignity Therapy: Final Words for Final Days.* New York: Oxford University Press.

Chochinov, H.M. (2012). *Dignity Therapy: Final Words for Final Days.* New York: Oxford University Press.

Chochinov, H.M., & Cann, B.J. (2005). Interventions to enhance the spiritual aspects of dying. *Journal of Palliative Medicine*, 8 (Supplement 1), S103–S115.

Cole, T. (1992). *The Journey of Life: A Cultural History of Aging in America.* Cambridge, UK: Cambridge University Press.

Coulehan, J. (2011). Deep hope: a song without words. *Theoretical Medicine and Bioethics*, 32(3), 143–160.

Curlin, F.A. (2015). Hospice and palliative medicine's attempt at an art of dying. In L.S. Dugdale (ed.), *Dying in the Twenty-First Century: Toward a New Ethical Framework for the Art of Dying Well.* Cambridge, MA: MIT Press, 47–63.

Doka, J., & Morgan, J.D. (1993). *Death and Spirituality.* Amityville, NY: Baywood.

Downing, G.M. (2011). "Who knows?" 10 steps to better prognostication. In Emanuel, L.L., & Librach, S.L. (eds.), *Palliative Care: Core Skills and Competencies* (2nd ed.). St. Louis, MO: Elsevier Saunders, 69–79.

Dugdale, L.S. (2015). *Dying in the Twenty-First Century: Toward a New Ethical Framework for the Art of Dying Well.* Cambridge, MA: MIT Press.

Emanuel, L., Bennett, K., & Richardson, V.E. (Feb 2007). The dying role. *Journal of Palliative Medicine*, 10(1), 159–168.

Emanuel, L.L., & Librach, S.L. (2011). *Palliative Care: Core Skills and Competencies* (2nd ed.). St. Louis, MO: Elsevier Saunders.

Erikson, E.H. (1959). *Identity and the Life Cycle.* New York: International Universities Press.

Ferris, F., Danilychev, M., & Siegel, A. (2011). Last hours of living. In Emanuel, L.L., & Librach, S.L. (eds.), *Palliative Care: Core Skills and Competencies* (2nd ed.). St. Louis, MO: Elsevier Saunders, 319–342.

Firestone, R.W., & Catlett, J. (2009). *Beyond Death Anxiety*. New York: Springer.

Fitchett, G., & Nolan, S. (eds.). (2015). *Spiritual Care in Practice: Case Studies in Healthcare Chaplaincy*. Philadelphia: Jessica Kingsley Publishers.

Ganzini, L. (Jun 2006). Artificial nutrition and hydration at the end of life: ethics and evidence. *Palliative and Supportive Care*, 4(2), 135–143.

Gawande, A. (2014). *Being Mortal: Medicine and What Matters in the End*. Toronto: Doubleday.

Harrington, D.J., & Matthews, C.R. (eds.). (2010). *Encountering Jesus in the Scriptures*. Mahwah, NJ: Paulist Press.

Hart, M.J. (2011). Spiritual care. In L.L. Emanuel & S.L. Librach (eds.), *Palliative Care: Core Skills and Competencies* (2nd ed.). St. Louis, MO: Elsevier Saunders, 584–598.

Hughes, J.C., & Baldwin, C. (2006). *Ethical Issues in Dementia Care: Making Difficult Decisions*. Philadelphia: Jessica Kingsley.

Hunter, K.M. (1993). *Doctors' Stories: The Narrative Structure of Medical Knowledge*. Princeton, NJ: Princeton University Press.

International Association of Catholic Bioethicists. (Autumn 2012). The use of sedatives in the care of persons who are seriously ill or dying. *The National Catholic Bioethics Quarterly*, 12(3), 489–501.

International Committee on English in the Liturgy. (1990). *Order of Christian Funerals*. Totowa, NJ: Catholic Book Publishing Company.

Institute of Medicine. (2001). *Relieving Pain in America: A Blueprint for Transforming Prevention, Care, Education and Research*. Washington, DC: The National Academies Press.

Janis, S. (2008). *Spirituality for Dummies*. Hoboken, NJ: Wiley Publishing Inc.

Jansen, L.A., & Sulmasy, D.P. (2002). Proportionality, terminal suffering and the restorative goals of medicine. *Theoretical Medicine*, 23, 321–337.

Jecker, N.S. (ed.). (1992). *Aging and Ethics: Philosophical Problems in Gerontology*. Totowa, NJ: Humana Press.

Jennings, B., Kaebnick, G.E., & Murray, T.H. (eds.). (Nov/Dec 2005). *Improving End of Life Care: Why Has It Been So Difficult?* A Hastings Center Special Report, S1–S61.

Johnson, E.A. (1998). *Friends of God and Prophets: A Feminist Theological Reading of the Communion of Saints*. New York: Continuum.

Kasper, W. (2013). *Mercy: The Essence of the Gospel and the Key to Christian Life*. Mahwah, NJ: Paulist Press.

Kass, L.R. (2002). *Life, Liberty and the Defense of Dignity: The Challenge for Bioethics*. San Francisco: Encounter Books.

Kaveny, M.C. (2005). The order of widows: what the early church can teach us about older women and health care. *Christian Bioethics*, 11(1), 11–34.

Kearney, M., & Mount, B. (2000). Spiritual care of the dying patient. In H.M. Chochinov & W. Breitbart (eds.), *Handbook of Psychiatry in Palliative Medicine*. New York: Oxford University Press, 357–373.

Kelley, M.M. (2010). *Grief: Contemporary Theory and the Practice of Ministry*. Minneapolis, MN: Fortress Press.

Kirk, T.W., Mahon, M.M., & Palliative Sedation Task Force of the National Hospice and Palliative Care Organization Ethics Committee. (2010). National Hospice and Palliative Care Organization (NHPCO) position statement and commentary on the use of palliative sedation in imminently dying terminally ill patients. *Journal of Pain and Symptom Management*, 39(5), 914–923.

Kleinman, A. (1988). *The Illness Narratives: Suffering, Healing and the Human Condition*. New York: Basic Books.

Kübler-Ross, E. (1969). *On Death and Dying*. New York: Scribner.

Lantos, J. (2015). Children. In L.S. Dugdale (ed.), *Dying in the Twenty-First Century: Toward a New Ethical Framework for the Art of Dying Well*. Cambridge, MA: MIT Press, 133–148.

Lazenby, M., McCorkindale, R., & Sulmasy, D.P. (eds.). (2014). *Safe Passage: A Global Spiritual Sourcebook for Care at the End of Life*. New York: Oxford University Press.

Liben, S. (2011). Pediatric palliative care. In L.L. Emanuel & S.L. Librach (eds.), *Palliative Care: Core Skills and Competencies* (2nd ed.). St. Louis, MO: Elsevier Saunders, 482–492.

Licona, M.R. (2010). *The Resurrection of Jesus: A New Historiographical Approach*. Downers Grove, IL: IVP Academic.

Liturgy Office of the Bishops' Conference of England and Wales and International Commission of Catholic Bishops' Conferences. (2005). *Rites of Committal for the Order of Christian Funerals*. London, UK: Burns & Oates, Sec. 9 (p. 4).

Lynn, J. (Nov/Dec 2005). Living long in fragile health: the new demographics shape end of life care. In B. Jennings, G.E. Kaebnick, & T.H. Murray (eds.), *Improving End of Life Care: Why Has It Been So Difficult?* A Hastings Center Special Report, S14–S18.

Macklin, R. (2003). Dignity is a useless concept. *British Medical Journal*, 327(7429), 1419–1420.

Martin, J. (2014). *Jesus: A Pilgrimage.* New York: Harper Collins.

McKnight, J. (1995). *The Careless Society: Community and Its Counterfeit.* New York: Basic Books.

Moody, H. (1992). *Ethics in an Aging Society.* Baltimore, MD: Johns Hopkins University Press.

Moses, S.N. (2015). *Ethics and the Elderly: The Challenge of Long-Term Care.* Maryknoll, NY: Orbis Books.

Musgrave, B., & McGettigan, N.J. (eds.). (2010). *Spiritual and Psychological Aspects of Illness.* Mahwah, NJ: Paulist Press.

Myers, J., & Chakraborty, A. (2011). Neurodegenerative diseases. In L.L. Emanuel & S. Librach (eds.), *Palliative Care: Core Skills and Competencies* (2nd ed.). St. Louis, MO: Elsevier Saunders, 435–450.

National Academies of Science, Engineering and Medicine. (2016). *Families Caring for an Aging America.* Washington, DC: The National Academies Press.

Navone, J.J. (1984). *Triumph Through Failure.* Eugene, OR: Wipf and Stock.

Neimeyer, R.A. (2000). *Lessons of Loss: A Guide to Coping.* Memphis, TN: Center for the Study of Loss and Transition.

Nuland, S. (1994). *How We Die: Reflections on Life's Final Chapter.* New York: Alfred A. Knopf.

O'Rourke, K.D. (1992). Pain relief: ethical issues and Catholic teaching. In K.W. Wildes, F. Abel, & J.C. Harvey (eds.). *Birth, Suffering and Death: Catholic Perspectives on the Edges of Life*. Dordrecht, Netherlands: Kluwer Academic Publishers, 157–169.

O'Rourke, K.D., & P. Boyle. (1999). *Medical Ethics: Sources of Catholic Teachings*. Washington: Georgetown University Press.

Pargament, K.I. (1997). *The Psychology of Religion and Coping*. New York: The Guilford Press.

Pearce, A., Clarke, L., & Pistrang, N. (2002). Managing sense of self: coping in the early stages of Alzheimer's disease. *Dementia*, 1(2), 173–192.

Pellegrino, E.D., Merrill, T.W., & Schulman, A. (eds.). (2009). *Human Dignity and Bioethics*. Notre Dame, IN: University of Notre Dame Press.

Polkinghorne, D.E. (1998). *Narrative Knowing and the Human Sciences*. Albany, NY: State University of New York Press.

Pontifical Council for Pastoral Assistance to Health Care Workers. (1995). *The Charter for Health Care Workers*. Vatican City: Vatican: no. 122.

Portenoy, R.K., Sibirceva, U., Smout, R., Horn, S., Connor, S., Blum, R.H., Spence, C., & Fine, P.G. (2006). Opioid use and survival at the end of life: a survey of a hospice population. *Journal of Pain and Symptom Management*, 32(6), 532–540.

Post, S.G. (2000). *The Moral Challenge of Alzheimer Disease: Ethical Issues from Diagnosis to Dying* (2nd ed.). Baltimore, MD: Johns Hopkins Press.

President's Council on Bioethics. (Sept 2005). *Taking Care: Ethical Caregiving in an Aging Society*. Washington, DC.

President's Council on Bioethics. (Dec 2008). *Controversies in the Determination of Death. A White Paper by the President's Council on Bioethics*. Washington, DC.

Puchalski, C. (2014). The spiritual care of patients and families at the end of life. In M. Lazenby, R. McCorkindale, & D.P. Sulmasy (eds.), *Safe Passage: A Global Spiritual Sourcebook for Care at the End of Life*. New York: Oxford University Press, 104–115.

Rahner, K. (1965). *On the Theology of Death*. New York: Herder and Herder.

Rahner, K. (1981). Growing old. In J. Griffiths (ed.), *Prayers and Meditations: An Anthology of Spiritual Writings of Karl Rahner*. New York: Crossroad.

Rando, T.A. (1984). *Grief, Dying and Death: Clinical Interventions for Caregivers*. Champaign, IL: Research Press Company.

Rolheiser, R. (2015). *The Passion and the Cross*. Toronto: Novalis.

Rosica, T. (2017). *The Seven Last Words of Christ*. Toronto: Novalis.

Sacred Congregation for the Doctrine of the Faith. (5 May 1980). *Declaration on Euthanasia Iura et Bona*. Vatican City: Vatican.

Saunders, C. (Jun 1981). The hospice: its meaning to patients and their physicians. *Hospital Practice*, 16(6), 93–108.

Shannon, T.A., & Walter, J.J. (2005). Assisted nutrition and hydration and the Catholic tradition. *Theological Studies*, 66, 651–662.

Sinclair, S., Pereira, J., & Raffin, S. (2006). A thematic review of the spirituality literature within palliative care. *Journal of Palliative Medicine*, 9(2), 464–479.

Sloan, J. (2009). *A Bitter Pill: How the Medical System Is Failing the Elderly*. Vancouver: Greystone Books.

Steinhauser, K.E., Christakis, N.A., Clipp, E.C., McNeilly, M., McIntyre, L., & Tulsky, J.A. (2000). Factors considered important at the end of life by patients, family, physicians, and other care providers. *JAMA*, 284(19), 2476–2482.

Sulmasy, D.P. (29 Nov 2010). The last word: the Catholic case for advance directives. *America*: http://www.america magazine.org/issue/757/article/last-word.

Thai, V., & Fainsinger, R.L. (2011). Pain. In Emanuel, L.L., & Librach, S.L. (eds.), *Palliative Care: Core Skills and Competencies* (2nd ed.). St. Louis, MO: Elsevier Saunders, 95–114.

Weiten, W., Lloyd, M.A., & Dunn, D.S. (2008). *Psychology Applied to Modern Life: Adjustment in the 21st Century* (9th ed.). Stanford, CT: Cengage Learning.

Wildes, K.W., Abel, F., & Harvey, J.C. (eds.). (2013). *Birth, Suffering and Death: Catholic Perspectives on the Edges of Life*. Dordrecht, Netherlands: Kluwer Academic Publishers.

World Health Organization. Cancer – WHO Definition of Palliative Care: http://www.who.int/cancer/palliative/definition/en.